The Perfect Transport

and the science of why you can't have it

Michal J A Paszkiewicz

2023

CRICETUS CRICETUS LTD

Unit A, 82 James Carter Road, IP28 7DE, UK

www.cricetuscricetus.co.uk

ISBN:

(hardback) 978-1-7393145-2-1 (eBook) 978-1-7393145-3-8

Acknowledgements

I would like to thank everyone who helped me review and refine this work – Marek Rembiasz, Esther Fairbairn, Joanna Fairbairn, Leo Murtagh, Steven Shaw, Hayley Bishop. They have all provided me with immensely helpful feedback. I thank Michael Davis for some last minute artistic advice. I thank Esther Fairbairn again for the illustrations that make the book more enjoyable and the splendid cover design. I thank my parents for making me the man that I am and I thank my wife, Ruth, who inspires me to be a better man.

I must also thank all my colleagues at Transport for London where I worked from 2015 to 2020 for helping me learn the many difficult topics on London's Transport. Special thanks must go to Nick Nurock and the rest of the Schools Outreach team who helped me broaden my horizons of interest in transport, and to Jason Blackford who gave me the opportunity to work on a variety of projects. A massive thanks must also go to the London Transport Museum and their library where I could find a multitude of books and materials to help me dive into transport topics that would have otherwise been inaccessible to me.

About the Author

MICHAL J A Paszkiewicz has a degree in Theoretical Physics and a Postgraduate Diploma in the relationship of Science and Religion. He worked for Transport for London for 4 years as a Software Developer, primarily on the Contactless Payment System. Since then he has spent 3 years leading a team building nautical cartography mobile applications for C-MAP, SIMRAD, B&G, and Lowrance. He runs a blog and occasionally gives lectures on transport and technology.

In his spare time, Michal loves to go on adventures with his 3 children, plays a variety of instruments, reads not enough books, dabbles in astrophotography, traps moths, and dreams about the next ski season.

www.michalpaszkiewicz.co.uk/blog/

Contents

Preface

T his book was actually ready for publication almost 3 years before I finally got around to publishing it. Unfortunately COVID-19 struck and lock-downs were introduced across the whole world. Many people talked about the world transitioning to some form of *new normal* or a change to our entire lives going forwards from this event. I therefore couldn't bring myself to publish a book that may no longer have relevance in the future.

The pandemic obviously had an immediate effect on transport - in some cases meaning that there was none of it. However, as restrictions have been slowly removed, the very same problems as always have come back, perhaps with a few differences, but nonetheless the same. My arguments and statements in the book didn't need rewriting. I won't claim that this is evidence that my book is timeless, but it certainly shows it may have considerable longevity. Either way I hope whoever reads this will still find it relevant in their time.

Introduction

Anyone who lives in London and perhaps anyone who lives in any extended urban area in the world will have found their everyday lives depend on many decisions of others. Often difficulties that one faces can be a result of decisions made by authorities that the person will never meet. People are faced with extremely long traffic jams, bans on noise during the night hours and rejections of planning permissions. As a result it may sometimes seem that the lives of urban residents are governed by some strange group of people who have no understanding of how real life works.

Growing up in London meant that I grew up with many judgements about the governing powers who affected my everyday existence. One of the governed structures that I found affected my life the most was that of transport.

In my early life I can remember countless traffic jams. Some of the worst were on the well-controlled border between Germany and Poland where every car's boot was routinely emptied out. The other worst were the ones just a few roads down from my house in London.

Secondary school meant I had to use public transport every day on my commute between zones 5 and 2. This proved especially troublesome with the central line closure of 2003, which meant I explored various alternatives – the overground trains and the Oxford Tube coach. In hindsight, the reasons for the closure were entirely understandable[1], but at

---

[1] A central line train derailed at Chancery Lane on 25th January 2003, injuring 32 people, after a motor became detached from a train. All lines using the 1992 Stock trains were temporarily closed till the fault could be determined and necessary modifications made.

the time, this was a massive hindrance to my school commute and led to much anger. This was especially so, because the newly introduced congestion charge meant that anything other than a car would be a cheaper form of transport. Alternatives to my usual travel route often took twice as long, while a day of light snow in the winter could mean a 4 hour return home instead of the usual 40 minute journey.

Until I started working in Transport for London years later, I never understood why the powers-that-be could not solve many seemingly trivial problems that I thought had such obvious solutions. Part of growing up for me was realising that my idealised understanding of how transport worked was a very poor model and needed refining with the hard truths of reality. I am not trying to press the idea that growing up is a matter of accepting society as-is. The alternative is true – we cannot accept things as they are. We must continually flourish and improve on the past. However, we can only do that if we thoroughly understand the current problems and how society has tried to deal with them in the past. I hope that this book will address many of the misunderstandings of society and authority that I had when I was younger, even though it is clearly too late for my past self to read this.

This book is intended to explain to the public why so many problems in transport remain unsolved. Hopefully this will alleviate some of the anger felt towards transport authorities the world over and help encourage a new generation of bright minds to join transport companies, agencies and government departments in the never-ending quest to the perfect transport system.

The book will begin with an ideal transport model. As the chapters progress, complexity will be added as assumptions will be challenged. Equations and mathematics will be kept to a minimum, but where they are present, the reader should not be worried if he doesn't understand what is going on. Everything will be explained verbally and skipping the maths will not stop anyone from understanding the contents of this book.

Please keep in mind that not many of the hypothetical parts of this book will represent transport strategies likely to be adopted by any transport authority. This should become clear as the book proceeds to shatter all illusions of simplicity in transport.

1.   Why are my trains so slow?

P<span></span>EOPLE enjoy liberty in many respects, and freedom of movement is one of the greatest freedoms one can enjoy. Walking, cycling and driving are all wonderful forms of transport that allow the person in control to go where they want whenever they want. When a person boards a train, there is not much they can do in terms of changing direction, route or speed – it can feel like you are at the mercy of the train operators, whether that be a driver, operator or automated control system. A short survey I conducted found that 76% of people are more annoyed if they are delayed while taking public transport than if they are delayed the same amount in private vehicles.

It can often feel frustrating when trains do not move as fast as one would like. Speeding up the trains would no doubt improve the rail service and ensure everyone gets everywhere on time. So why are the trains so slow? Surely if they were all sped up, we would all be able to get to our destinations faster and everyone would be happier. This chapter will try to explain why trains are faced with many limits to their speeds and why that would be difficult to change. It will also try to propose some solutions as to how we could solve some of these problems and explain why they are unlikely to be considered.

1.1 Ideal Train

Let us try to imagine an ideal train. Not only does it have the grand look of steam trains, it also has no carbon footprint and will serve free drinks and food at the on-board restaurant. The chandeliers hanging from the ceiling will beautifully light the armchairs that passengers can relax in on their journey. Or maybe the reader will have some other imagination of how the perfect train will look and feel, but the main important considerations in this section will be the technical ones.

This train will have a straight rail between two stations, with no obstacles. The train has an engine made of unobtainium that means it has no technical issues to travel however fast it may need. The only limit will be that of the passengers' ability to deal with acceleration.

A typical person can withstand 4g accelerations[1] - that is, 4 times the force one feels from the pull of the earth. Any faster and the passengers could lose their vision or even consciousness. Tests have shown that most pilots can last for over 4 minutes at 4.5g accelerations[2], which is far more time than we will need at any point in this discussion, especially considering we will be looking at a slightly lower acceleration. For now, we will have to pretend that we have figured out how to keep the chandeliers safe and that we can get the food and drinks to the passengers and ensure they can consume it safely and without any spills at these accelerations.

---

[1]The Wikipedia article on G-force induced loss of consciousness is excellent: https://en.wikipedia.org/wiki/G-LOC#Thresholds

[2]Truszczynski O, Wojtkowiak M, Lewkowicz R, Biernacki MP, Kowalczuk K. Reaction time in pilots at sustained acceleration of +4.5 G(z). Aviat Space Environ Med. 2013;84(8):845-849. doi:10.3357/asem.3490.2013. https://www.ncbi.nlm.nih.gov/pubmed/23926661

The way to reach the second station from the first station in the least amount of time would be to constantly accelerate. However, the train would then be travelling much too fast at the second station for the passengers to get out. Safety is everyone's number one priority in transport systems, so we will have to reject this model already. For the train to stop at the destination, but still travel as fast as possible, it would have to accelerate for exactly half the journey and then to decelerate with the same, but opposite force for the rest of the trip. The unfortunate consequence of such a journey will mean that any passengers facing forwards for the first half of the journey will be more comfortable than others, before being launched off their chairs. On the second half of the trip, the rear-facing passengers will finally get a chance to have a better journey than those facing forwards at the point that the train starts to brake.

Let us consider this ideal train travelling across some distances that are regularly travelled within London. We will continue assuming that these journeys are on a straight, unobstructed rail. The longest distance between two adjacent stations on the London Underground as of 2018 is Chesham to Chalfont & Latimer on the Metropolitan line at a whole 6.3km. With our 4g acceleration, we would travel across this in just over 25 seconds. House prices in Chesham would rise drastically, and town planning authorities would be put under a lot of pressure to turn green belt land into housing. Luckily we are only worrying about transport problems in this book and we can cause economic mayhem around the stations in our hypothetical scenarios without having to face the responses of angry citizens.

The shortest distance is between Leicester Square and Covent Garden on the Piccadilly line – at just 300 metres[3]! This shorter distance would

---

[3]https://www.whatdotheyknow.com/request/distance_between_adjacent_underg

8

be covered in about 5.5 seconds - about a fifth of the time it would take to travel the longest journey, even though it is less than a twentieth of the length. Indeed we find that the first section of the distance is covered in far more time than the rest of the distance – quite obviously, since the train will get a chance to move at a higher speed if it is given a longer distance to cover.

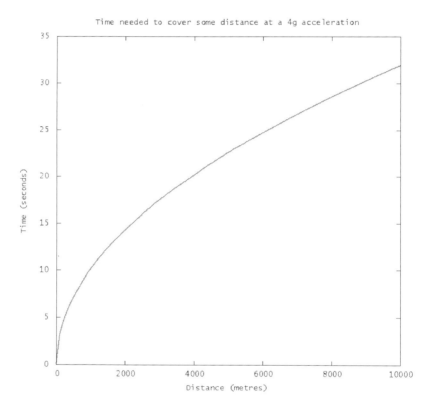

Figure 1.1: The time taken to move a certain distance when travelling with a 4g acceleration.

If the distances between stations are greater, the train can move faster and a greater distance can be covered in a short amount of time. Transport authorities need to decide on trade-offs between placing convenient station locations and ensuring they are far apart enough to ensure trains can cover a considerable amount of distance in a set time to ensure passengers can travel far in a decent amount of time[4]. Central London has many stations that are very close together. It is often quicker to walk between the stations than to navigate the tunnels, wait for a train, travel on the train and walk out of the tunnels, even while walking up and down the escalators. Videos of passengers leaving a train at one station, running and getting back on the same train at the next station have gone viral a few times and leave everyone wondering whether the actors have not realised that normal behaviour on the London Underground involves standing or sitting very still and trying not to disturb any fellow passengers.

With 4g accelerations, most distances between any two adjacent stations would be covered within 15 seconds, which would cut travel times considerably and hopefully stop the actors in the videos from putting the noble trains to shame.

Unfortunately 4g accelerations aren't very practical in real life. There is still a slight chance someone could pass out, and these accelerations are only feasible for the body if passengers are seated facing the correct way and properly strapped in. In a typical train, it can be expected that there will be standing passengers. Many of the standing passengers will be reading a book or looking down at their latest electronic gadgets without holding onto any railings. Some passengers may even be walking across the train while it is moving. Occasionally one can even come across passengers that walk around playing various instruments, while the others in the carriage actively try to pretend they haven't noticed

---

[4]https://www.citymetric.com/transport/speed-vs-coverage-how-do-metro-systems-decide-how-space-their-stops-3308

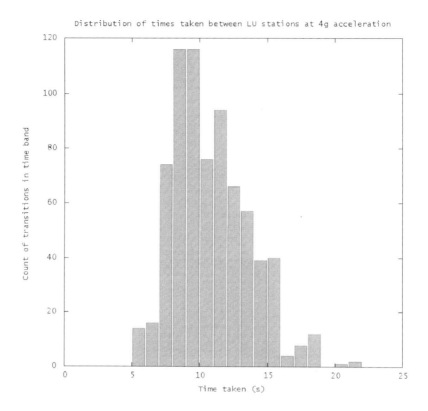

Figure 1.2: This figure shows the distribution of how quickly London Underground trains could get between stops if they were travelling with a 4g acceleration.

while soaking in a bit of the free entertainment at the same time. These moving passengers are some of the most unstable of the passengers and therefore they provide the realistic limit as to how much the train can accelerate.

Considerable study has been carried out into passenger stability against longitudinal acceleration[5]. Best practice guidelines don't usually allow a

---

[5]J P Powell, R Palacin Passenger Stability Within Moving Railway Vehicles: Limits on Maximum Longitudinal Acceleration (2015) https://link.springer.com/article/10.1007/s40864-015-0012-y

greater acceleration than $1.3m/s^2$. This changes our times substantially.

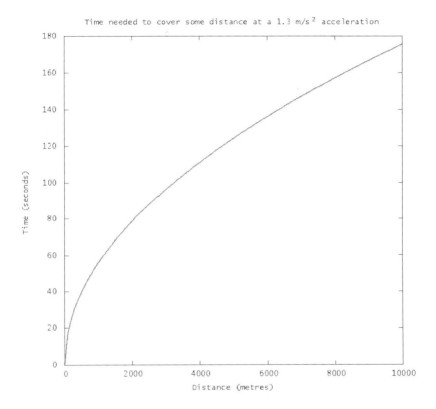

Figure 1.3: The time taken to move a certain distance when travelling with a $1.3m/s^2$ acceleration.

Our longest and shortest distances are now covered in about 139 and 30 seconds respectively. The vast majority of journeys between two adjacent stations on the Underground would then take under 80 seconds. This is much longer than our travel time at 4g accelerations. While 4g accelerations may be unrealistic, this should highlight the fact that speed of transit is sacrificed for the convenience of passengers within the train, who may wish to stand up or walk about. If this freedom were to be removed, trains could travel between places faster.

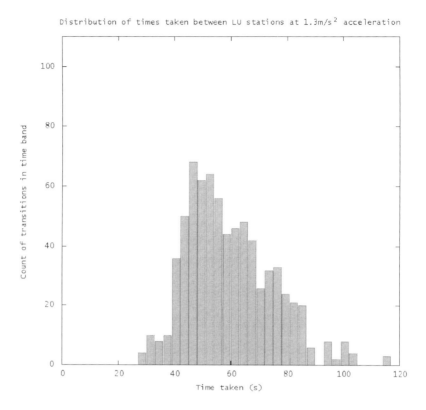

Figure 1.4: This figure shows the distribution of how quickly London Underground trains could get between stops if they were travelling with a $1.3 m/s^2$ acceleration.

Many cities do not have the luxury of having few short distances between stations. Higher acceleration would benefit these lines more, as the trains would reach much higher speeds over the longer routes. The urban train line in Melbourne has a longest distance between stations of 10.45km, between Newport and Laverton. At $1.3 m/s^2$, this would take almost 3 minutes, while 4g this would have been covered in less than 33 seconds.

Inter-city trains can have much greater distances between stations and there are of course trains that travel immense distances between

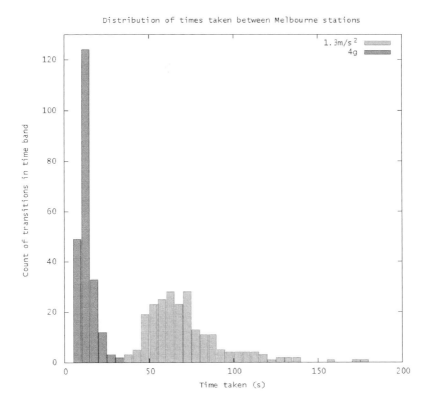

Figure 1.5: This figure shows the distribution of how quickly trains could get between stops in Melbourne.

stops. A trans-Siberian journey from Chita to Birobidzhan is over 2152km long and would take almost 8 minutes to travel at 4g and 43 minutes at $1.3 m/s^2$. We will see later that such accelerations are not feasible for such long distances due to technical realities, but maybe one day we will have technical solutions for everything and a journey across the trans-Siberian express could take hours instead of the week it currently takes.

Comparisons between transition time distributions are slightly more obvious on train lines which do not have as wide a spread in distances between stations. For example, the longest journey at 4g accelerations across the Glasgow Subway would be about four times as fast as the shortest journey on that network at $1.3m/s^2$.

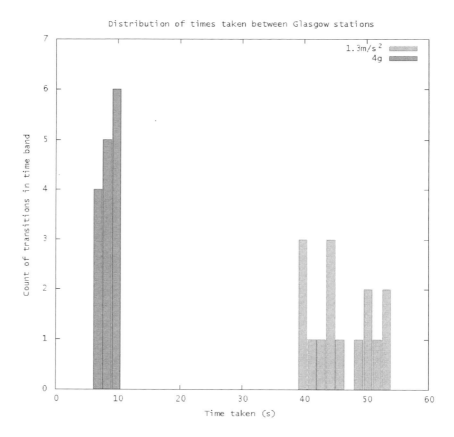

Figure 1.6: This figure shows the distribution of how quickly trains could get between stops in Glasgow.

So far, we have been looking at the upper bounds of human tolerance of accelerations, but that is not really acceptable in public transport. Trains need to provide sufficient comfort, which can be as important to passengers as their journey time lengths. If we look at slightly more comfortable accelerations, we can find that a $0.45m/s^2$ constant acceleration seems to estimate the distribution of current unimpeded travel times for the London Underground fairly well. Lower accelerations will generally keep passengers on their feet and stop them from flying into each other.

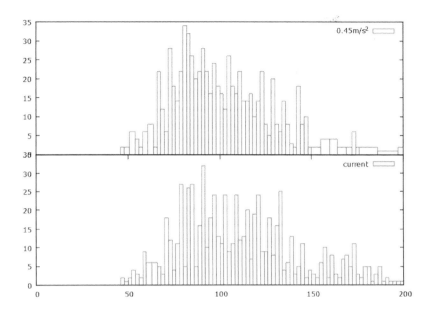

Figure 1.7: A distribution of how many trips between stations travel in various amounts of time. The comparison is between an idealised train accelerating at $0.45 m/s^2$ and real times taken from LU data.

The interesting thing about the current system's similarity to a $0.45 m/s^2$ constant acceleration model is that we know that the trains can't be accelerating any less than this amount, since speed cannot be reached without some acceleration. Therefore it isn't possible to get equal or better times without at least matching the constant acceleration of our model. $0.45 m/s^2$ is actually a considerably high acceleration for a train and puts London Underground trains on the world stage in terms of acceleration of trains. Other high speed trains across the world perform similarly. For example, the high speed train between Tianjin and Beijing[6] has an

[6] http://www.railway-technical.com/books-papers--articles/high-speed-

average acceleration of $0.46m/s^2$, but breaks at $0.4m/s^2$.

1.2   Constant Acceleration Travel

High acceleration travel is already done on rollercoasters, which elicit euphoria by providing high accelerations. Passengers are held in by firm *belts* which stop them falling out or causing injury to themselves. Small rollercoaster-style *cars* could be a form of transport for the future – they would especially benefit if they decoupled from the main rail at stations, allowing trains to continue moving on the main rail if they did not need to stop at particular stations, while giving passengers sufficient time to strap in to the slightly more complex *belts*. This would require multiple points on the rail next to the station where the small *cars* can switch between rails. Cars that are in front on the rail wouldn't block those behind from getting back on the main rail. Whichever car was ready to leave first, could do so without waiting for other passengers on the platform.

There are also other problems with being strapped in a high-acceleration scenario. What happens if someone drops their phone or glasses? They will be unable to go and get them, while they may just continue flying off into the distance, unless the shuttles are fairly small and contained. There would also have to be consideration for passengers who may need to put some luggage away in lockers that would stop bags becoming a safety hazard for the passengers.

Wheelchair users and people with small children may also have problems – how can the disabled be expected to jump between a wheelchair and a rollercoaster style seat? One possible solution could be to learn

railway-capacity.pdf

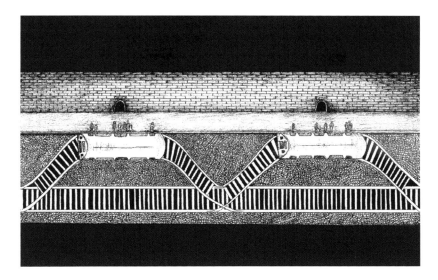

Figure 1.8: Allowing decoupling of small *cars* on a rail instead of stopping a whole train would allow more cars to pass by if passengers didn't need to stop there. This would be even more efficient if they were sorted into the *cars* upon entry by desired destination.

from the ISOFIX idea. ISOFIX is a standard clip in cars that allows children's car seats to be clipped into the car easily and providing a firm anchor to ensure the seats cannot move in the event of a crash. ISOFIX became mandatory throughout the European Union in 2011 and is generally considered a success story that has greatly benefited parents and children. If transport was to transform across a nation, continent or the world, it is reasonable to assume that governments could subsidise and enforce policies or standards that would improve the safety of public transport users. Adaptors between wheelchairs and high-acceleration shuttle seats could be developed. Adaptors between buggies and high acceleration shuttle seats could be developed. ISOFIX clips could be present on all seats as alternatives to the *safety belts*. This would transform transport for the disabled and for parents – it would be a simple matter of arriving, clipping in, travelling and then clipping out at their destination.

One of the problems with a system that relies on proper fastening for the safety of passengers would be that this would require a suitable amount of supervision. Hopefully much of this could be automated – checks on whether seatbelts are fastened on seats that have had substantial wait placed on them is already a feature of many modern cars. However, to efficiently load passengers on such a transport would probably require a substantial amount of transport staff to help out with boarding and ensuring the safety of the passengers. A need for staff and supervision becomes even further clear when it is considered that people may not feel safe in a public setting with severely restricted freedom of movement. Fear of assault or robbery could otherwise be increased, as passengers already strapped in would largely be at the mercy of any malicious passengers who had not yet strapped in. CCTV camera numbers may need to be increased, along with numbers of CCTV monitoring staff. This may further dampen appreciation of the system which would become far more intrusive in the monitoring of passengers.

1.2.1 Market Interest

To try to get a vague understanding of whether anyone would be interested in high-acceleration travel, I ran a poll asking whether people would prefer lower times of transit between stations, or whether they prefer their freedom of movement on trains. The poll lasted a week and had 51 participants. The results are summarised below:

	Lower transit times	Freedom of Movement
Female	3	12
Male	17	19
Total	20 (39%)	31(61%)
Weighted Total	33.6%	66.4%

The weighted total takes into account that there were fewer female participants in the study, so it inflates the female result.

It is fairly clear that the majority of people prefer their freedom of movement to lower transit times. Interestingly there is quite a gap between collective male and female opinions on the topic. Women were 4 times more likely to prefer freedom of movement than lower transit times, while men were only marginally more likely to do so.

Of course, this poll was flawed in many ways. It could have definitely been improved with more participants, split over more criteria and ran as a multivariate analysis. The poll was also entirely hypothetical, which means that the voters had not experienced the high-acceleration transport style. But we cannot be sure that if they had it would have improved their likelihood of voting for it. It could just as well have made the 39% prefer traditional trains after all. However, it remains true that such opinions could change depending on future trials and it might be possible that one day higher acceleration travel could be considered more normal and not disapproved of by the public.

1.2.2 Freedom of Usage

Another point that should be raised at this point is that not everyone has to take any particular mode of transport. If high-acceleration trains were provided, the passengers who prefer their freedom of movement could still pick a different form of transport that would satisfy their likes and desires. Those who were in more of a hurry could pick the trains that get them to their destination faster while people who like to enjoy a calmer ride could pick a more traditional form of transport. The older transport systems should have a reduced load if new infrastructure is created for the more modern versions, meaning that everyone should benefit from introducing such services.

Currently this is not an idea on most transport authorities' agenda though. Most transport authorities are trying to be fair and open to diversity. Transport that everyone can take and benefit from with joy is something that any sane governing body will aim for. Implementing the high-acceleration transport could be seen as an investment that is preferential to a set of people. In our case, men would be far more likely to travel on the new trains. Why should men be given preferential treatment over women in transport investments? That would be immoral and suggestive of an existence of a ruling patriarchy. The division of transport based on preference and tolerance of adrenaline levels raised by high accelerations may unfortunately have to be left to utopian science fiction stories.

1.3 Limited by Speed

In reality, our scenarios would unfortunately be rather limited by the maximum possible speeds for trains. It is hard to sustain great speeds due to air resistance, and engines struggle with too much speed. The fastest trains do not use engines in fact, but are powered by electromagnets that push the train along using magnetic repulsion. Magnetic Levitation (Maglev) trains can go very fast – the Shanghai Maglev can go at 267mph. While our $1.3m/s^2$ accelerating train would only have reached a top speed of about 142mph and therefore would have been quite achievable for a maglev train, the 4g train would have had to peak at just under 790mph – just over Mach 1. Crossing the sound barrier takes a lot more power, due to a sudden increase in aerodynamic drag. We have also learnt from the Concorde project that running at such high speeds can be incredibly wearing on the object that is traveling and therefore would require very high maintenance costs. The sonic boom is also undesirable in urban areas. Overall, even if we could get a train to travel that fast, it wouldn't make sense to allow trains to do so anyway, unless we somehow develop a whole new range of technologies that deal with these problems and make this sustainable.

Since we know that the longest distance between stations on the London Underground would not allow a train accelerating at $1.3m/s^2$ to breach the maximum speed limit, we can be sure that any train accelerating at this rate through London would not be troubled by technical difficulties in terms of reaching the maximum speed if they used a Maglev train. In fact, as of 2018, the UK already uses trains that can reach much higher speeds[7]. But let us pretend that it would be easily feasible to replace all standard rails with maglev rails. Our model would now change to one where initial acceleration is constant, until a maximum speed is reached. At this point, the engines are no longer able to accelerate and the train will continue to travel until the point at which it can safely decelerate again to a stop at the next station.

The distance travelled while accelerating at 4g to the full speed of a maglev and back down to 0 again is about 363m, which is completed

---

[7]The Eurostar e320, which entered service in 2015 can reach 200mph, for example. https://en.wikipedia.org/wiki/British_Rail_Class_374

in 6.1 seconds. With the limit of this maximum speed, any further distances will now be completed at an additional steady speed of 119.4m/s. Long distance journeys now would take considerably longer, but the train still covers distances up to 10km in half the time or less than it would if it was accelerating at $1.3m/s^2$.

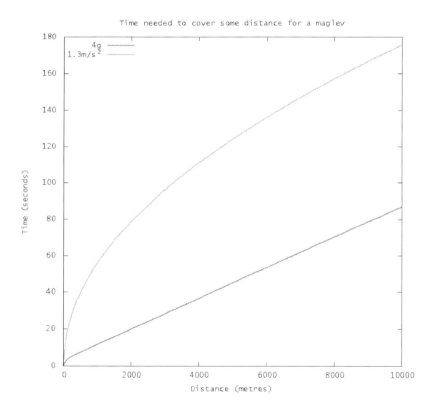

Figure 1.9: The time taken to move a certain distance when travelling with various accelerations on a Maglev train that is limited by the maximum speed of 267mph.

The 2152km trans-Siberian journey from Chita to Birobidzhan would now take 5 hours instead of 8 minutes at a 4g acceleration, and only just over a minute longer with the $1.3m/s^2$ acceleration. It is pretty clear that with longer distances, maximum acceleration plays less of a role and it is the maximum speed that makes the biggest difference in transit times. The land speed record as of 2018 is ThrustSSC's 1228km/h. It travelled a mile at this speed in October 1997 and hasn't been beaten since. If the trans-Siberian express could travel at this speed, it would cover the distance in just over a third of the time that the maglev takes.

Most urban metros still have fairly short distances between stations on average. The average station distances of the 212 biggest metro systems mostly fall under 2km, so can save a considerable amount of time between most of their stations by increasing their accelerations. It may not be an improvement as good as postulated earlier, but it could still be an improvement. The main problem with changing maximum accelerations remains the fact that acceleration is felt by passengers and any increase in acceleration results in further discomfort for passengers.

Galilean relativity states that laws of motion are the same in all inertial frames. This is a slightly complex way of pointing out the fact that passengers on a train moving at a constant velocity do not feel much different than if the train had been stationary (apart from the noise and view out of the windows). Provided the rails are sufficiently smooth, increasing maximum speeds of trains will not have any negative effects on passengers. Travelling at very high speeds still allows passengers to eat and drink without a need for any complex tableware. Balancing games like Jenga could be played without much disruption from the train itself.

All in all, maximum speeds stop transport authorities from improving transit times between stations to the immense extents they could be improved by otherwise. There are of course many other limits of engineering equipment that will not allow an indefinite improvement of transit times. Maintenance costs can change depending on the speed that trains operate at – minimising these costs can save a network a vast

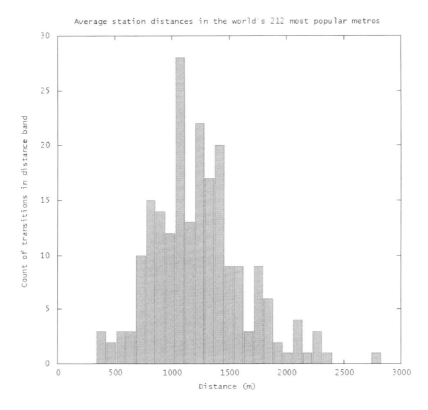

Figure 1.10: The distribution of average distances between stations in the world's 212 most popular metro systems.

sum of money. Engines also often have optimum speeds at which they will require the least power per mile to run at. Saving energy on public transportation is particularly important, because these systems are used constantly for most of the year. Any energy savings will make dramatic differences in energy bills and the carbon footprint. The rails that the trains run on can also be a limiting factor. We will next examine how turns in a rail can stop us from reaching the top speeds that trains can normally reach.

1.4   Limited by Turns

Unfortunately not all railway lines are straight. Turns in railway lines stop trains from travelling at arbitrarily large speeds, as there is a risk for derailment. To calculate the maximum velocity at which a train can navigate a turn, the following equation can be used:

$$v = \sqrt{rg \tan \theta}$$

Where r is the curve radius, g is the gravitational acceleration (9.8) and θ is the angle of the tilt of the track that the train is on. The smaller the radius of the curve and therefore the tighter the turn, the slower the train can approach it. The only way to try to increase the possible speed going around a turn is to increase the angle of inclination. If a track leans in to a turn, the train can approach it at higher speeds. The cant of a rail cannot be too great though, as that would mean that the train may not be able to stop on the turn without tipping over and derailing. Tilting trains which lean in to turns on ordinary straight rails are another option for allowing faster speeds on turns. These provide the advantage that they can adjust the amount of tilt they need for a turn depending on the speed they are travelling at.

The sharpest turn on the London Underground is called the Caxton Curve[8] and is situated on the Central Line, right next to Shepherd's Bush station. Its radius of just 60m means that even with a 10 degree inclination, trains wouldn't be able to go past this turn faster than 22mph (10m/s). Passengers often recognise the Caxton Curve - even though they do not know the name – by the horrendous screeching emitted from the pressure of the wheels on the rails.

---

[8]http://underground-history.co.uk/woodlane.php

Unfortunately most urban train lines aren't as straight as one would expect[9]. Building underground railways in old cities like London usually involves considerable work in planning how to avoid deep building foundations, sewers, archaeological sites and sub-surface rivers. Overground lines rely on an ownership of a large amount of connected land, which is rarely owned in neat, straight lines. Public bodies that build railways sometimes have to result to forcing homeowners to give up their properties with Compulsory Purchase Orders, which can be painful for the homeowners and expensive for the authorities. When railways are expanded or connected, desired destinations rarely line up in straight lines and there will always be some turns in order to reach more populous or advantageous locations. A large amount of turns on a rail can also cause problems for trains. Trains that go around a circle on radial lines in urban systems often have disproportionate amounts of wear on the wheels if they always go in the same direction[10].

1.5   Limited by Jerks

Part of the problem with passenger stability is not just acceleration, but the jerk. Jerk is a measure of change in acceleration – putting the brakes on suddenly is far less comfortable than travelling at a constant deceleration for some time. In our scenario, our constant acceleration couldn't begin instantaneously, but would have to be increased from 0 at a slower rate. Acceptable levels of Jerk can change depending on the acceleration. With our $1.3 m/s^2$ acceleration, if we want the vast majority of passengers to remain stable, the jerk would have to be less than $1 m/s^3$. If we try to

---

[9]https://www.whatdotheyknow.com/request/224813/response/560395/attach/3/ London+Connections+Map.pdf

[10]p.66 Martin, Andrew Underground, Overground

take a conservative jerk of $0.5m/s^3$, this would now mean that from rest, we would only be able to reach our maximum acceleration after 2.6 seconds. Similarly, it would take a similar amount of time to turn down the final deceleration to the resting point at the destination.

Jerk is not just a result of intentional acceleration though. It can also be a result of irregularity of the rails. A small irregularity in the track can cause quite a lot of jerk, since trains are quite reliant on the smoothness of their tracks and are particularly at threat from oscillations if irregularities line up at regular intervals. Problems with irregularities cannot be entirely avoided with rails. Even a hypothetical perfectly straight metal rail will end up increasing in length with a higher temperature, which can result in bends being created at various points. Engineers get around this problem by not using continuous rails, but by having lots of rails joined together with holes in between. These joints can be covered up, but it is still a small irregularity that can be felt in a rigid train. Passengers can be protected from these irregularities by improving suspensions. Use of rubber-tyres on trains has also proven successful in various places such as the Paris Métro. Trains that hang from a rail instead of standing on one can also help smooth out a journey, but they come with another load of costs and problems. Maglev trains hover, which means they are not affected as much by inconsistencies on their route. Unsurprisingly, journeys on maglev trains are some of the smoothest in the world.

1.6   Limited by Power

The maximum amount of acceleration we can get from a train can be estimated fairly easily. This should show us whether our high acceleration proposition is at all feasible with the existing machinery being built in the world. We can look at how powerful some of the strongest trains are and try to see whether any of them could achieve our slightly ridiculous acceleration of 4g. As of 2019, the 3 most powerful locomotives are the Shenhua Mining Group HXD1 (19,310hp) and the Russian 2ES10S (17,701hp) and 4E5K (17,594hp). These locomotives weigh 276, 300 and 392 tonnes respectively. So our first candidate should surely be of most interest to us, as it not only has the most power, but it also is the lightest of the three.

The power of our locomotive tells us how big the work output of our locomotive can be. This does not necessarily tell us how much pulling force the train will have. Horsepower is proportional to the product of the Torque and the Rotational Speed. This means that if you can't change your horsepower, if you want your wheel to rotate faster, you will not achieve a very high torque. Similarly, if you want to increase torque, the rotation speed of the wheel will not be as fast. Torque is the rotational equivalent of normal, linear force, which is in fact equal to the Torque divided by the radius of the wheel the torque is applied to. What this means is that naturally, as the speed of the wheel increases, the amount of torque that can be applied to it decreases, so engines and motors do not generally produce constant forces or accelerations.

In fact, what is more interesting to us in this discussion is the tractive force – this is the maximum amount of force that the locomotive can exert on the surface it is on. The HXD1 has a tractive force of 1,140kN. Since the locomotive has a mass of 276 tonnes, we can calculate that the maximum acceleration it could achieve would be $1,140,000/276,000 = 4.13m/s^2$. This is about a whole magnitude lower than our hopeful acceleration of 4g. If the locomotive were to pull some carriages, or seat

people on top of it, this maximum possible acceleration would only decrease. However, such a train could easily pull many typical passenger
carriages at much higher accelerations than are currently used. For example, the weight of a 1992 Stock train carriage is between 20.5 and 22.5
tonnes. Such a carriage can carry 116 people at full capacity. The average
human weighs about 62kg[11]. This means that the passengers on such a
carriage can weigh about 7.2 tonnes by themselves! So, let us say that the
average full 1992 stock carriage weighs about 28 tonnes. If we have 8 of
these carriages, that is a total weight of 224 tonnes, and our locomotive
could pull itself along with these carriages at an acceleration of $2.28m/s^2$
(if we ignore the friction of the carriage wheels). This is quite a bit more
than the previously considered safe limit of $1.3m/s^2$ and would therefore
require a safe way of strapping passengers in. Having a second locomotive would double the tractive force and only increase the weight of the
train by the weight of the locomotive, giving us a maximum acceleration
of $2.9m/s^2$. If each carriage had motors, this force could further increase.
Due to this fact, it seems that one could keep adding locomotives to continually increase the acceleration. If we consider different amounts of
locomotives pulling carriages of the weight proposed before, we arrive
at the following equation for maximum acceleration:

$$a = \frac{1,140,000N}{276,000N + 224,000}$$

Where N is the number of locomotives pulling our carriages.

From this equation we can see that as the number of carriages increases, the tractive force (the numerator of our equation) may increase
linearly, but the weight of the train (the denominator of the equation)

---

[11]But the average Briton is heavier, with the average male at 83.6kg and the average
woman at 70.2kg https://www.bbc.co.uk/news/uk-11534042

also increases linearly, with the added weight of our carriages. When N is small, it can make a large difference to the acceleration, but as more locomotives are added, the maximum acceleration will tend to and never exceed an acceleration of about $4.13m/s^2$. How disappointing.

If we consider the two Russian locomotives previously mentioned, we notice that they actually have higher tractive force than the HXD1. The 2ES10S has a tractive force of 1176kN, while the even heavier 4E5K has an even higher tractive force, rated at 1356kN. Why do these heavier trains have a higher tractive force? This largely boils down to the amount of friction, which is related to the weight of the locomotive and is the subject that will be discussed next.

1.7   Limited by Friction

Even if you had an engine with the greatest possible power, there are further limits to the acceleration you can reach on a conventional rail due to the laws of physics. Conventional rail relies on wheels turning on rails in order to generate forward momentum. The force that drives the train forwards is therefore the friction between the wheel and the rail. Now the maximum amount of frictional force that can be applied between two objects can be calculated by a basic equation:

$$F_f = \mu F_n$$

Where F_n is the normal force (or the force applied perpendicularly between the two objects) and μ is the coefficient of friction.

In the case of most trains, the normal force happens to be the weight of the train, or at least the weight of that part of the train that has the engines. This is the force that presses the train upon the tracks. Force is also the mass of an object multiplied by its acceleration, so we know that in our case the magnitude of the normal force is the mass of the train above the pulling wheels multiplied by the gravitational pull on earth's surface – about 9.8 (or g).

Now the masses in the two forces F_f and F_n are not necessarily the same. For example, trains driven by single locomotives suffer from the fact that the locomotive is the only part of the train that is doing any pulling. This means that the mass in F_n is only that of the locomotive, while the mass of F_f is that of the whole train. By putting this information into the equation above and rearranging it, we can get an equation for the maximum possible acceleration without slipping:

$$a_{\text{max}} = \frac{\mu g \, m_{\text{locomotive}}}{m_{\text{train}}}$$

Now the case would always be that the mass of the locomotive would be smaller than that of a train. In modern trains, we can put motors in all the carriages[12] which means that the mass of the locomotive becomes the same as the mass of the train, but $\frac{m_{\text{locomotive}}}{m_{\text{train}}}$ can never be more than 1. Our acceleration can therefore only ever be bigger than $1g$ if μ could be more than 1.

Unfortunately most coefficients of friction are between 0 and 1. There are a few materials that offer higher, but not usually by much. For example, the coefficient of friction between aluminium and itself can be as high as 1.35 and for the coefficient between silver and itself we have 1.4. But if they become even slightly lubricated, this drops off rapidly to 0.3 and 0.55 respectively[13]. It should be pretty obvious now that trains

---

[12]About 2/3 of carriages per London Underground train have a motor, although Central Line trains only have half of the carriages equipped with motors.

[13]https://www.engineeringtoolbox.com/friction-coefficients-d_778.html

will perform worse in rain or in winter where there may be ice or snow. But on a horizontal surface, using normal, flat materials for wheels and tracks will restrict conventional trains to only theoretically be able to reach about 1.4g at most, and that is if every wheel is powered by a motor. Flat surfaces are not the only option though. Sand paper uses the fact that it is not flat to create more friction and therefore to be able to wear down other surfaces to make them flat. Finding a material that could work as sandpaper between wheels and tracks is very difficult. The weight of the train and the fast movement of the surface of the wheels means that the material would be flattened very quickly and therefore make the material ineffective. Even so, the sandpaper effect is sometimes used to help out trains. When it snows or rails can be icy, a locomotive sandbox is often used. This sandbox drops sand onto the slippery rail in front of the train's wheels as the train moves down the line. In urban scenarios, sandboxes are not often attached to all trains, but there will be sand-trains that would travel around in the morning, covering all the rails with sand to help the other trains that do not have sandboxes. This can help with traction, but is not really an option for everyday trains. If some amount of sand was dropped on the rails every day, the tracks would eventually become a long sand dune, unless there were also regular services to remove the sand. The sand can also be detrimental in dry conditions, where it can become an additional layer of material that can slip on the rail.

There are of course technological advances that can circumvent our problem. One way is to have a rail that can be *hugged* on either side of the rail by a wheel. The force on the rail from the wheels could then be adjusted by how tight the two wheels clamp down onto the rail. This clamping force would be an additional force on top of the weight, creating a much stronger normal force, in a bigger contact surface area, meaning that the maximum force from friction can be drastically increased. Another alternative is to have teeth in the tracks, and to switch the wheels out for gears. The force applied on the track by the wheel then becomes more of a pushing force instead of a frictional force, which would allow for greater forces. Unfortunately, putting teeth into miles of rail would make the manufacturing process of rails quite a bit more complex and would require much greater detail in machining. This means that such an option would result in a much greater cost and could have more maintenance problems in the long run.

Another option is the option of avoiding friction altogether – maglev trains do not use friction to travel, instead relying on magnetic propulsion to levitate them to their destinations. This means that the limits of friction do not apply in this case. Other forms of propulsion that do not use friction also exist – jet propulsion and rocket propulsion. Jet propulsion can be discarded due to the fact that it is both inefficient in comparison to conventional motors for pulling trains along tracks and also due to the problem of jet propulsion sucking air through the jet at such speeds that it could pull passengers off platforms and cut them up in the blades. Rockets are also not a suitable form of propulsion for trains. Anyone who didn't make it onto a train would be promptly burnt up in the fires of the rocket or die due to the exhaust fumes.

It should be clear now that to improve on conventional rail infrastructure, accelerations higher than $1.4g$ are not achievable without immense infrastructure costs. Such high accelerations are also not necessarily a good idea - for example, if you assume that you can brake at a $1.4g$ deceleration, you could be surprised by a wet section of track that would slip for attempted forces greater than $0.5g$ and therefore result in going straight past a platform, crashing into an object ahead or derailment around a tight turn in the rail.

Real brakes in railways usually also have profiles that are far more complex than the simple scenario we have been looking at. For example, the coefficient of friction μ_s in cast iron brake blocks is given by the following equation:

$$\mu_s(V, N_s) = 0.6 \frac{V + 100}{5V + 100} \frac{\frac{16}{g} N_s + 100}{\frac{80}{g} N_s + 100}$$

Where V is the linear velocity of the wheel in km/h, N_s is the normal force acting on a brake block in kN and g is the gravitational acceleration.

This coefficient of friction is highest when the normal force and velocity are smallest, but even then the coefficient will not exceed 0.6. This means that even if the contact between wheel and rail had a coefficient of friction as high as 1.4, the brake itself may not be able to sustain such friction and the wheel will still be turning, making the high coefficient of friction with the rails ineffective. As velocities and the force of the brake increase, this coefficient of friction will only become smaller, adding further limits. As a result, trains using cast iron brake locks brake in two stages – an initial stage with enough braking pressure to initially slow down the train, followed by a stage with a much higher braking pressure once the train is slow enough to not make the coefficient of friction fall too low[14].

[14]Effects of Braking Characteristics on the Longitudinal Dynamics of Short Passenger Trains (2017) by Cătălin Cruceanu, Camil Ion Crăciun, Ioan Cristian Cruceanu. Referenced from Rail Transport – Systems Approach (Studies in Systems, Decision and Control volume 87) p.8.

1.8 Optimising Ideal Train Throughputs

When considering transport solutions, something that is more important than the potential speed of one person's journey is the concept of traffic flow. Fast trains do not necessarily mean that everyone going on a journey will get to their destination in a timely fashion.

For example, let us consider 5000 passengers who want to travel a certain distance one morning and all arrive at the same time. The train they are taking is fast and has a capacity of 1000 people. Unfortunately it only comes once an hour. This means that 20% of the passengers won't even manage to board a train for 4 hours even if they all arrived at the time of departure of the first train! And if the journey to the final destination took 1 hour, the average journey time for all 5000 passengers would have been 3 hours. So a train that was twice as slow but had a capacity of 5000 passengers would have got everyone to their destination far quicker – in just two hours. Alternatively, if the trains came every half an hour, but still took an hour to get to their destination, passengers would have still arrived at their destination on average in two hours. The big difference between the two solutions is that the slower train would have a slower best case scenario. The first passengers would have taken two hours to arrive instead of one. However, the slower train would have also had a faster worst case scenario. The more common trains would have resulted in some passengers taking 3 hours to get to their destination.

The average travel time per passenger can be calculated by the simple equation:

$$T = \frac{1}{2}\left[2t + (\frac{P}{C} - 1)W\right]$$

Where C is the passenger capacity, t is the time the train takes to travel to the destination, P is the total amount of passengers and W is the waiting time between trains. To improve the average travel time per passenger of this railway line, the rail authorities would want to minimise the value of T. This could be done by reducing the time taken to travel by improving train speed, by increasing the capacity of the trains by adding additional carriages, by decreasing the waiting time between trains by adding more trains to the service, or by decreasing the total amount of passengers by encouraging them to take other forms of transport.

1.8.1 Changing Passenger Behaviour

While it is obvious that decreasing the amount of passengers taking public transport may make that form of transport more pleasant for others, it might be less obvious that the behaviour of the passengers can also improve the experience. In our above example, if the passengers had not arrived all at once, but 1000 of them had arrived per hour, the original hourly trains with a capacity of 1000 would have given an average time taken per passenger of 1 hour. In fact, the more spread out the departure times of passengers, the easier it is to organise and deal with the service. But how can such a spread be encouraged?

Journey planners can be very helpful with these things. If passengers are shown how much of a wait time they are likely to have for a train and provided with alternative forms of transport, this can change their behaviour. The success of GPS systems that show traffic on roads is a testament to this. Journey planners that map routes across cities also usually show delays on services and suggest ways of avoiding them. Many of these could be improved if given information on platform overcrowding and train capacities. This one directional information is not particularly useful for train operators though, who will not know if passengers' behaviour will change until the journeys have already started taking place. Behaviour upon such information cannot be always well predicted. For example, knowledge of a busy platform could mean that all the passengers decide to leave early to counteract the time delay and thereby cause further overcrowding or delays. As real-time information is fed to passengers, this changes their behaviour, which then changes the information itself. It is very possible for a crowd to try to chase a gap in crowding, with the gap disappearing the moment the crowd arrives. If there are passengers constantly arriving at the various options independently of those following the information, this crowd could potentially be stuck in a limbo between travel options.

A small poll run with 35 people where they were asked whether information on crowding for their journey would change their behaviour on their journeys showed astounding results. 91% of the people asked stated that they would change their behaviour if given crowding information. Further research could be launched into how much these behaviours would change and how much it could help to equalise crowd levels between modes of transport. Either way, it is clear that such information can definitely change behaviours and may have some potential towards improving passengers' journeys.

Another way of changing the behaviour of passengers is to use financial means. This is particularly clear from past data – Ken Livingstone introduced the *Fares Fair* in 1981, which reduced bus and tube fares by a third. This increased the use of public transport by half a million passengers. A year later, the fares were doubled and the number of passengers on public transport was reduced by a million[15]. Such reaction to fares makes it pretty clear that pricing can truly affect behaviour.

By making fares more expensive at busier times, passengers can be encouraged to travel when the service is under less strain. However, such changes in fares are disadvantageous for passengers who have to travel at peak times and may feel that they are being overcharged. Not only would people with typical working hours be targeted by the hike in fares, but the fares would also be affecting the poor the most. Is it fair if poor passengers are forced to take longer routes than the richer ones due to the cost of the fares? A fine balance between fares that can change behaviour and fares that retain passengers' goodwill has to be met, which is a very tough challenge for fare setters. Fare discounts that are beneficial to some customers are also not always fair to all customers. For example, annual season tickets which provide a big discount over shorter-term tickets can be seen as unfair to the poor, because they assume that the person buying the ticket will have the full amount – which can be quite costly – upfront. Recent improvements in technology have allowed the use of pay-as-you-go travel with rules that cap costs of journeys over days and weeks, which is more beneficial to frequent passengers who may not have the financial means to pay for an annual ticket upfront.

Advance purchased tickets on rail systems can also be very useful. They can change cost depending on how busy a particular time is, but the tickets also give advanced warning of which times will be extremely busy and can prompt a train operating company to add carriages to trains at that time or to add additional trains. It is not always possible to spread the arrival of many passengers, such as when a big event has ended near a local station, such as a football match or concert. Advanced

---

[15]p.244 Martin, Andrew Underground, Overground

warning can be incredibly useful in such situations and allows suitable preparation. The tickets are often cheaper the further in advance they are bought. This encourages passengers to plan further ahead and gives train operators more time to prepare.

Advance tickets come with their own problems as well though. If someone decides not to take the train after all, not only will they have been charged for a service they didn't use, but there will also be an empty seat on the train that could have been filled. Rail operators that plan around ticket sales can also find themselves with problems if one of their trains goes out of service. If their trains were set up to only accommodate the ticket holders, the subsequent train will be overcrowded unless they can somehow manage to scrounge another train from somewhere in a short amount of time.

Fares authorities have to be especially careful when they set the fares. Often surprising effects can come from applying a particular set of rules. For example, Ken Livingstone's introduction of London's system of zoning increased the use of public transport, simply because it was a simpler system with fewer gradations, meaning that it could be understood more easily by commuters.

1.8.2 Increasing Capacity

Trains have the amazing capability of adding or removing carriages, which means that it is quite easy to increase or decrease the capacity of a train. Unfortunately there can be other hurdles that make this problematic. Small platform sizes can mean that additional carriages become unusable. Even carriages that easily allow passengers between them do not solve this problem, as too many passengers in any carriage that blocks the movement of further passengers to a viable set of doors can cause chaos. Train operators also need to be mindful that they do not have needlessly long trains. Any additional carriage means additional fuel used, increases the train's carbon footprint and makes accelerating and braking more taxing on the engines and brakes.

1.8.3   Adding Trains

Adding trains to a line is another way train operators can increase the throughput on their services. This is of course the most expensive of all of the options. Transport for London's order of 192 S7 and S8 stock trains cost a total of £1.5 billion. Naively divided up, that comes to just under £8 million per train. But cost isn't the only problem that comes with an increased number of trains.

As train density on a line increases, the returns on added further trains become smaller and smaller[16]. More trains also make operations harder. Keeping track of many trains is difficult, especially in bendy tunnels that restrict drivers' visibility and may lack signalling technology that would keep a rail operator up to date with the exact location of all trains.

Safe distances have to be maintained between trains, which with more trains can be restrictive on the speed. The faster the trains go, the greater the distance that has to be kept between trains. With many trains come many safe distances and speeds may have to be kept lower.

A slow train can also be the limiting factor for all the trains on that line, as trains are often unable to overtake other trains. Technical faults with a single train can cause a delay on a whole line and so train oper-

---

[16]Andrew Smith, Phill Wheat and Michal Wolanski Public transport operations costs from Chris Nash' Handbook of Research Methods and Applications in Transport Economics and Policy (2017) p.59

ators will try to remove faulty trains from a line as quickly as possible. But our idea of adding additional trains means that we have many more trains that can become faulty at any point, meaning that we are adding a significant risk of delays on the whole line due to train faults if we keep adding more trains. About half of all of London Underground's delays are due to faults with assets[17]. Companies like Transport for London already put considerable work into trying to fix issues before they arise. Data scientists have used machine learning to help predict when assets may need maintenance[18] and therefore guide engineers to investigate and fix the potential issues. Even so, faults in trains have not been entirely eliminated and the risks of adding trains will still remain.

One way to make sure that a train on a rail does not delay all the other trains on the line would be to ensure that each direction on a line has 2 rails instead of one, with frequent points where trains could switch between the rails. Faulty trains could then be avoided by the trains behind. The additional cost of rails and tunnels would be immense, but the main problem for the service would be that there would then be twice as many points on the rails that need maintenance, and these are some of the assets that fail the most in rail systems.

---

[17]It is unsurprising, considering the amount of assets and mechanisms that are involved – even the simplest railway would have a multitude of different objects with different lifespans. Concrete sleepers can last up to 50 years and the rail itself will most likely last about 25 years, but the ballast underneath could be washed away or moved due to subsidence in less time. See John Glover's Principles of Railway Operation (2013) Ian Allan Publishing p.17 for a further discussion.

[18]https://www.computerworlduk.com/data/how-tfl-is-using-predictive-analytics-keep-underground-running-3671541/

1.9 Loading Times

One of the biggest factors in keeping urban trains slow is the passenger disembarking and embarking times. Trains can often spend as long unloading and loading passengers onto trains as they do travelling between the stations.

To get London's Victoria Line to get 36 trains per hour through each station, not only did Transport for London have to improve the signalling system considerably, but they also needed station staff to help encourage the passengers to get on and off the train in a timely fashion. Also importantly they needed to stop passengers trying to get on trains once the trains were ready to leave. Making passengers aware that the next train is just behind in the tunnel and is most likely less crowded can help passengers decide not to try to get on an already packed train. Passengers trying to get onto crammed trains can stop the doors from closing, which means that the train cannot leave and there could be a delay to the service.

London Underground trains are very well designed to help optimise movement between the trains and the platforms. They have large doors, and the newer S stock trains allow movement all the way down through the train, which means that passengers should spread throughout the train instead of overcrowding particular carriages. One of the most difficult situations with unloading and loading trains is when both the train and the platform are overcrowded. Transport for London encourages people to let passengers off the train first before trying to board. But many frequent passengers who travel at peak hours can tell of their experiences where passengers only just about managed to get out of the train before the doors closed, allowing no passengers on the platform to get on. Unfortunately there isn't much of a better alternative. It may be true that it would make sense to make space on the platform by loading the train if the platform was overcrowded but the train was fairly empty. However, it would be far more distressing for passengers to be stuck on a train and travelling further than they need to than it would for a passenger to not manage to get on a train. The passengers that travel too far would have to come back on the next return train, which would cause further crowding and add further issues. Waiting longer for passengers to get on, if the passengers getting off have already taken a long time is also not always a great option, as every minute the train stays at the station and does not let the next one get there can cause delays and overcrowding on the whole line instead of just this one platform.

Some technical solutions that have not yet been tried in London would be some form of electronic system that could tell passengers on a platform which carriages have more space on approaching trains. This could help passengers prepare to board carriages that they might be able to board, instead of taking a blind guess as to whether their location will be useful for boarding the next train. Green lines on the floor showing where train doors are have been trialled in some stations. Feelings were mixed about these trials – some experienced commuters were upset by the fact that they lost their competitive advantage in boarding the trains[19]. Questions were also raised as to whether the trial was designed well, since it was not very clearly communicated that commuters were supposed to avoid waiting on the green lanes[20]. If these ideas are to be tested scientifically, some of the points raised should be addressed

---

[19]https://www.standard.co.uk/news/london/experienced-commuters-fuming-as-tfls-green-platform-paint-spoils-competitive-advantage-a3633566.html

[20]https://diamondgeezer.blogspot.com/2017/07/green-lanes-trial.html

and featured in new versions of the trials. An electronic notification system could a future step of such trials. One problem that could occur with such a system could be that passengers may all crowd around a single carriage, overcrowding that space and blocking much of the platform, instead of evenly spreading across the platform. If the notifications showed more or less how much space was available, this could potentially minimise such a scenario, by only encouraging enough and no more passengers to crowd around a spot.

Going back to the high acceleration transport options mentioned earlier, one of the considerations with trains that require special sorts of *belts* to keep the passengers safe would be the fact that unloading and loading times could take a lot longer. Having small *cars* that are decoupled from the main rail could allow passengers to unload and load at their own leisure without delaying the whole line, and provided there are enough of them, they could ensure some passengers were always getting on and off them. The model of having lots of small *cars* may make the reader wonder at this point why we could not just remove all the rails and replace them with actual cars.

1.10   Rail over Roads

Trains are much safer than cars[21]. This isn't very surprising, considering they only usually have (more or less) one degree of freedom, so don't swerve between each other adding risks. Modern rail is also usually protected mechanically and often with considerable automated systems that prevent crashes. Sections of rail can have their lights turned red and their power removed automatically if the train ahead is too close.

---

[21]http://news.bbc.co.uk/1/hi/uk/3991753.stm

Fully automated trains are also miles ahead of self-driving cars in terms
of safety, with far fewer technical issues. Automated trains do not need
to use visual recognition if platforms are shielded from the rails, so the
systems on the automated trains do not have to solve problems that are
quite as complicated as those of autonomous cars.

Trains also have the benefit of being placed fairly securely on rails,
which minimises the chance of them going sideways off the path. Firmer
attachment to rails, such as those on rollercoasters also shows how trains
could also hold tightly to rails and immensely increase the safety of
transport by minimising the possibility of derailment.

Trains running in urban environments could also not easily be replaced by cars. Lines that mostly run through fairly tight tunnels would
be a major risk for vehicles that run on petrol or other flammable fuel.
A terrifying example of this risk is that of the Mont Blanc Tunnel fire of
1999, where 39 people died as a result of a truck catching fire in the tunnel. Escape for other drivers proved impossible as smoke blinded them
and caused engines to stall because of lack of oxygen. Urban metro lines
are often a lot tighter than the Mont Blanc tunnel, so may be even more
dangerous in similar scenarios. One solution to this problem would be
to only allow fully electric vehicles into the tunnels. This would not be
feasible as of 2019, where most cities have not got enough electric cars
in them. There are only about 12,000 electric vehicles registered in London[22]. These would only carry about 50,000 people at a time at most,
so would not be a viable option of replacing the 543 trains operational
at the time, which can carry almost ten times as many people. It would
maybe be possible to try to allow them on one particular line, but it

---

[22]https://www.london.gov.uk/sites/default/files/environment_committee_-
_ev_report.pdf

would require many changes – ripping up the tracks, changing stations to allow passengers to get into the cars. This is assuming that suddenly all of the private owners of the electric cars want to donate them to public transport – rather unlikely. The transport authorities would have to buy new fleets of electric cars, and running a trial would be vastly expensive due to the amount of vehicles required to be bought along with the infrastructure changes. The time during which a rail would be replaced by cars would also be very disruptive to the passengers who rely on that line every day.

1.11   Costs

Of course, one of the biggest challenges for transport authorities is to be able to cover the costs of projects. Many of the ideas mentioned in this chapter have been presented without their costs attached. This was an attempt to show that the problem of decreasing transit times between stations is not a simple one, even without all the difficulties of managing complex signalling systems and the need to deal with various unpredictable problems on train lines. A few simple back-of-the-envelope estimates will now be presented to try to show how much the various ideas could cost if they were implemented as of 2019. We will use the London Underground as the case study for improvements.

1.11.1   Maglev Trains

The Japanese Chuo Shinkasen is a maglev line between Tokyo and Nagoya. The cost of the line came to about £140 million per km of line . The London Underground is 402km long as of 2019, so the total cost would come to about £71 billion. About 90% of Chuo Shinkasen will be underground, so the costs are probably fairly representative of what they could be for London. On the other hand, London's Crossrail project is currently estimated to cost £15.4 billion, for 118km of upgraded or built rail. That comes to about £130 million per km of line. Transport authorities have to decide often on whether they need to expand or upgrade existing infrastructure. The decision to bring in Crossrail is a response to the increasing demand on current public transport in London. The introduction of Crossrail is estimated to decrease the congestion on the Central, Jubilee, Bakerloo and District Lines by *between 20 and 60 percent*[23]. Upgrading the current lines to use maglev trains instead of building new lines would not have a sufficient difference on current capacities within London, so is unlikely to be considered as important as the building of new railway lines.

What may be surprising to the reader is the fact that the cost per km between maglev and Crossrail does not differ much. Operational costs are also interesting, in that maglev trains require more energy to run at low speeds (as would be experienced most often in urban areas) than conventional trains, but these costs are offset by the fact that maglev trains require less maintenance. This is due to the fact that they are levitating, which means that there is less wear and tear on the train and on the track. Why would authorities pick conventional rail instead of maglev then for the consideration of this new project?

There are many reasons for picking conventional trains over maglev trains, such as the fact that the trains could be reused or resold easily in Europe, where the rail gauge is already conventional and would not require much change to move the trains between various tracks. Keeping to conventions also helps engineers, who are already experienced in

---

[23]between20and60percent

running conventional rail lines, so would not require much additional training for maintaining a train that requires entirely different technologies.

1.11.2 Rollercoaster style trains

One of the propositions in this chapter was the idea of small trains that would run at high accelerations. Restraints on the carriages would keep passengers safe. The trains would decouple from the main rail at stations and therefore load passengers in smaller groups, keeping loading times down. The costs of such a transport are hard to estimate, due to the fact that it is not something that has been built before at such scale. The main costs would undoubtedly be the costs of upgrading the stations to have multiple rails where the trains could decouple and to build loading bays so passengers can board safely and efficiently. Upgrades to tube stations can be extremely expensive. The upgrades to bank station, which will be completed by 2022 have cost about £600 million[24]. These upgrades include expansions to escalators and building travellators to improve passenger movements across the station, as well as building a new tunnel to modernise the northern line. Such upgrades are not particularly invasive, especially in comparison to our rollercoaster-style trains which will require additional tunnels and tracks for all lines per station. If we take a guess and assume that the cost of the current bank expansions could be an estimate for an average per station, the cost of upgrading the stations would be about £162 billion for London[25]

---

[24]https://www.ianvisits.co.uk/blog/2018/10/09/behind-the-scenes-at-london-undergrounds-bank-tube-station-upgrade/

[25]This is a huge cost in comparison to existing projects. For example, the Deep Tube Upgrade Programme is going to cost £16.42 billion and should increase the capacity of the London Underground by 30%. It is planned for delivery between 2024 and 2033.

The change would be so invasive to the transport system that lines will have to be closed for the duration of the upgrade. We can calculate the costs of loss of fare revenue quite easily. If we assume that each line would on average, have to be closed for 1 year for the changes, we can estimate that the cost would be Transport for London's normal fare revenue for 1 year. This would come to £4.8 billion. However, additional costs would be inflicted upon businesses in London, which would suffer due to so many transport closures. These sorts of losses would probably be similar to the lower end costs of tube strikes to the economy. Tube strikes can cost the economy between £10m and £300m per day[26]. If we assume that it is just £10m/day (since planned closures should allow planning ahead to deal with problems), that still comes to about £3 billion per year of money lost in London's economy. The closure of the Central Line in 2003 was estimated to cost London's economy about £275 million[27] for a closure of just 11 weeks. Over a year, this would have cost £1.3 billion. Adjusted for inflation, this would be about £1.95 billion, which isn't too dissimilar to our estimate from losses due to tube strikes, especially if one considers that this amount would be higher 15 years on, due to the fact that London now has definitely got more businesses and trade.

Another cost that definitely needs to be estimated is the cost of shorter trains with advanced *seatbelts* that can keep passengers safe. Currently there are 543 trains that take between 506 (Waterloo & City 1992 stock) and 1176 (Metropolitan line S8 stock) passengers. If we take the average of 841, we can guesstimate that there could be a total capacity throughout London of about 450,000 passengers on the trains at a time. We can

---

[26]https://www.telegraph.co.uk/business/2017/01/09/much-will-londons-tube-strike-cost-economy-will-damage-capitals/

[27]http://news.bbc.co.uk/1/hi/uk/2941527.stm

50

assume that theme park owners have optimised loading times for their
trains, so we can predict that if we want to optimise loading times, we
need to use trains of a similar capacity. At a glance, modern rollercoasters (such as Alton Towers' Wicker Man) are being built with trains that
take 24 riders per train, with 2 people abreast along twelve cars. To load
450,000 people into trains of capacity 24, this would take about 18,750
trains. Unfortunately rollercoaster construction companies refused to
give me a quote for 18,750 rollercoaster trains to seat 24 people each –
I assume they thought I was insane. We can try to get a very rough estimate though. Let us say that a 24-seating train will be built of say 6
carriages with 4 seats each. Now each of these carriages will probably
be slightly less complex than a car, but it will also lack the economy of
scale – 18,750 carriages cannot compare well to the scale of the millions
of cars sold by major automobile companies. So let us assume that one
of our carriages costs a similar amount to the base price of a Volkswagen Up (a European 4-seater car). As of 2019, this car can cost as little
as about £10,000[28], meaning our trains could cost about £60,000 each,
bringing our total cost to about £1.125 billion for the trains.

Signalling for this new form of transport would also be a major cost.
It would be a far more complex signalling system than those of any existing railway sing it would require much higher precision and greater
safety assurance. To assure safety for systems of such complexity, it
might be necessary to use formal methods. These are mathematical techniques that verify software and hardware systems, which theoretically
ensure that systems meet specifications exactly. Such a system could
easily rack up even up to a billion pounds, especially if extended testing phases are included. However, such a system could also prove very

[28]Unfortunately Volkswagen are not sponsoring this book

valuable if it was to be successful and could be resold to other cities. A major problem with procurement for such a system would be that there would be far too many unknowns and risks. It would not have been done before, especially not at this scale. It would be an immense amount of money to invest without clear assurance that it would definitely work without any further costs. It might not even work at all. If it does work, it might not work as well as expected. Knowledge of how well it could work may just not be available until such a project is finished. These risks would probably sway the decision against building such a system for most transport authorities.

Additional staff would also be needed to ensure everyone was strapped in safely. Even if this came to just a few additional staff per station, this would be a considerable additional sum for running the service. If this was even on average just 3 additional staff per station working at London Living wage, this would come to about £15million per year. There would also be a need for additional engineers to maintain the additional trains and tracks and line operators to ensure the service was running smoothly. People would be unwilling to work at London Living wage for these jobs, so these jobs could easily cost additional tens of millions.

All in all, replacing existing trains with our rollercoaster-style trains in London would be likely to cost about £166 billion. The signalling system would most likely have to be funded, built and trialled first; otherwise the entire project would be at risk. Until someone can spare a few billion pounds for these trials, such an idea is unlikely to see the light of day and it is pretty clear why – we already know how to add infrastructure without so much risk with pretty good predictions as to the impacts on transport.

2.   Why can't we just have more roads?

R OAD traffic is one of the greatest problems in transport, especially in areas without trains. City transport authorities are trying out drastic techniques to cut down traffic. These range from park and ride sites (where drivers are encouraged to park outside a city and use public transport into the city) to congestion charges (where drivers must pay additional taxes to use popular roads). Other extreme options have also been attempted. In Beijing, new car purchases are restricted by making potential owners compete for a purchase licence in a lottery. This may not be an option (currently) available to the liberalist west, but the sentiment seems to be shared in cities across the globe.

But why are authorities making life more difficult for drivers? Can't they add roads and therefore surely decrease congestion by increasing road space? Are they out of their minds?

This chapter will look at why additional roads do not necessarily help drivers, authorities or the traffic in general. Hopefully it will give some insight as to why strategies to deal with traffic often seem punitive, even though they are in fact remedial measures. We will explore ideas, some of which will be obvious, but others will seem very counter-intuitive.

Hopefully this chapter can paint a picture of how chaotic road traffic can be, why it is difficult to manage, and what approaches we can take on trying to improve traffic problems.

2.1 Funnelling

To begin with, it would be important to understand a few fundamentals about traffic flow and how congestion occurs. The simplest scenario is probably that of a straight road with some form of bottleneck at a point in the road. The same effect we see in a funnel – where water in the funnel builds up, due to the small diameter at the bottom of the funnel – is what causes many traffic jams. We will now try to explore this in a bit more detail and explore what effect road widths have on traffic.

Let us imagine a motorway that goes from a point A to a point B. Let us suppose that we have an infinite amount of cars trying to go from A to B via this motorway. They have some arbitrary maximum speed and follow each other closely to try and maximise the amount of cars going between the two locations. In this case, the amount of lanes on the motorway really matters. Twice as many lanes means you can get twice as many cars between the two points and ten times as many lanes would increase the traffic flow tenfold. Now if at any point on this motorway some lanes are closed, we realise that the traffic flow is limited to the traffic flow at that bottleneck[1]. The motorway before the lane closure may also seem congested, because the cars will have to go slower before

---

[1] For the sake of simplicity, we will ignore the fact that a bottleneck's capacity decreases after congestion has set in. This occurs in both vehicle and pedestrian traffic – further reading can be found in Hoogendoorn and Daamen's A Novel Calibration Approach of Microscopic Pedestrian Models from Harry Timmermans' Pedestrian Behavior: Models, Data Collection and Applications (2009) Emerald p.211

the bottleneck to allow cars from the multiple lanes to now share the smaller amount of lanes afterwards. Because of this, we find that where we have a constant high supply of vehicles, the speed of vehicles on any road is limited by how fast we can get vehicles through the slowest parts of that road.

The case with infinite cars in lockstep obviously doesn't mirror reality. However, it provides a way to analyse how a section of road performs when there is more traffic than that section of road is designed for. Most of the time (or at least at night time), roads with bottlenecks will not cause traffic, as the vehicles will not be in lockstep. They will be travelling far enough from each other that they will be able to navigate lane closures or sections of road with lower speed limits without affecting the areas with higher speed limits. We also have different kinds of roads for different purposes – motorways are long distant roads that cars will go on to reach a destination that will be off that motorway and most likely down some smaller roads, through which fewer cars will be travelling as less people on the motorway will be trying to go to that location.

In this section, we are interested in improving traffic flow for areas that are already congested (otherwise, why would we be thinking about building more road space?). Our aim, judging by the question is to improve traffic for a finite number of cars in a certain space. But when we are making these improvements, we can still use our model with an infinite supply of cars to try to figure out how much the traffic flow is improving. If we were to get some actual metrics to figure out how the traffic will improve in scenarios for the actual amount of people on those roads, then we would have to consider how many cars there are on those roads, but an infinite supply should simplify this section for the reader.

We are going to ignore speed limits on roads for now, because it is obvious that a higher speed limit means a higher traffic flow, but we cannot do away with speed limits – they have been put there for public safety and should be respected. Our primary concern will be road design and whether it can be improved.

We know that by adding lanes to a road we can improve traffic flow. However, adding lanes to a section of a road only makes sense if there aren't any other sections of the road that would slow the traffic flow for the rest of the road. So if we have a 3 lane motorway that goes from A to Z, adding a lane between Y and Z would not improve the traffic flow of the whole road, as only the vehicles that manage to get through A to Y will be able to make it through Y and Z. However, at this point this lane can offer extra space for the vehicles that made it through A to Y, but since they would have been going at their maximum speed through the bottleneck already, they won't be able to travel at any higher speed. Cars going the opposite way – from Z to A – may end up travelling slower, as they are held up by the bottleneck at Y where the vehicles would have to merge onto fewer lanes. So direction of travel makes a big difference on how traffic flow is affected by additional lanes.

Additional lanes on the section Y to Z of our motorway could also be important, if that section of the motorway is used more. For example, if there was a 1 lane slip road going onto the motorway at point Y, with another infinite stream of cars joining on at that point, the traffic flow would have actually increased, because these cars would not have been slowed by a thinner section of motorway beforehand – the new 4 lane section of motorway would behave as if it had been a 4-lane motorway up till that point.

Most roads are not just motorways. Roads have traffic lights, crossings, junctions and various other points where traffic may become blocked up. In some of these cases, additional lanes can help considerably. For example, where there is a junction with another road featuring traffic lights. If additional lanes are provided on either side of the traffic lights, then every time the light changes to green, more cars can get across the lights, increasing the traffic flow across that junction and helping all the vehicles that have not yet arrived at that junction.

2.2 Braess' paradox

We have discussed adding lanes to roads, but what about adding independent roads to the networks? Often, additional roads can help with traffic significantly. For example, bypasses are roads that avoid built-up areas that may be the destination of a large amount of vehicles. Before a bypass is built, many people trying to navigate a route that goes a lot further are slowed down by the fact that they have to go through the built-up area. People travelling to the city, town or village may also be slowed down by the people trying to pass through. And the inhabitants of the area will be slowed down by both groups of people that have to drive into their area. By building a bypass, authorities can encourage people who are just driving through, to avoid a busy area altogether. These people will have less traffic there and will probably have fewer traffic lights and crossings. Anyone who wants to travel inside the built-up area will then also not have to face the traffic due to the people that were just going to pass through, so everyone wins. Protests, such as those seen during the Third Battle of Newbury, largely involve the dissent involved with felling trees or damaging environment in some other way – few people would disagree that bypasses help with congestion.

If bypasses work so well, can we then assume that you can always bypass any congested area? Roads with major traffic problems often have a single bottleneck. If this bottleneck could be bypassed, would that not solve the problem with the congestion on the whole road?

Dietrich Braess, a German mathematician was wondering about such conundrums when he realised that sometimes a shortcut could make traffic worse[2]. To understand why this could happen, we are going to have to understand a few basic concepts from a branch of mathematics called Game theory.

Game theory is a study of behaviours in simplified scenarios that try to figure out optimal solutions for the various players involved. Its name is particularly apt, as it fits well into studying board games or other strategic games and can determine winning strategies. Game theory has also historically been used to help understand many real world problems, such as the Cuban Missile Crisis and the Economy.

When playing games, such as Chess or Poker, one tries to make the best move possible. But the best move possible also has to consider the decisions that opponents or competitors make. For example, when playing chess, a grandmaster will consider what impact a potential move will have by analysing the best moves his opponent could make in response to the move. Only once a grandmaster has analysed a number of best moves for both players will the grandmaster finally decide the move is strong enough. In Poker, when one has a good hand, it makes a lot of sense to raise the stakes. However, a good Poker player will also need to consider what hands his opponents might have been dealt – his hand may be good, but there is a chance someone could have a better hand.

Game theory has shown through mathematical analysis that the fact

---

[2]Über ein Paradoxon aus der Verkehrsplanung , Braess Dietrich, http://homepage. ruhr-uni-bochum.de/Dietrich.Braess/paradox.pdf

that one should consider competitors' moves can result in situations where all competitors make decisions that are least optimal for them. A perfect example of this is in a problem called the Prisoner's dilemma.

The Prisoner's dilemma is a game that models the situation where two members of a criminal gang have been arrested, kept separate, have been read the Miranda rights and given an offer. If neither of them talk, they will both be put in prison for a year. If one of them betrays the other, the betrayer will get to go free, while the betrayed will go to prison for 3 years. If they both betray each other, they will go to prison for 2 years each. For any prisoner, we can summarise the result of either betrayal or silence in the following image:

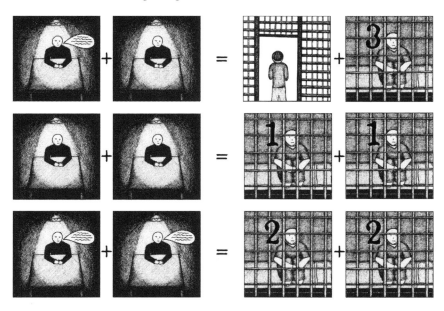

Figure 2.1: The Prisoner's dilemma. If one suspect speaks up, he walks free and the other one spends 3 years in jail. If they both stay silent, they stay in jail for one year. If they both speak up, they both spend 2 years in jail. The best result as a total is for both to stay silent, but to avoid spending 3 years in jail each suspect has strong motivations to speak up.

Now what is particularly interesting in this scenario is that for the two prisoners combined, the optimum solution would be if they both didn't talk – between the two of them they would only spend a total of 2 years in prison. While a single betrayal is beneficial for the betrayer, together the prisoners would spend a total of 3 years in prison, so it is a worse situation in total. If both prisoners betray each other, the total time spent in jail between the two of them is 4 years, so it is in fact the worst scenario. However, if each prisoner considers the move that the other prisoner may take, the situation usually results with them betraying each other, meaning they arrive at the least optimal solution. The reason for this is that as far as a prisoner is concerned, if the other prisoner betrays him, they will have to spend 3 years in jail. This is the situation where they would have to spend the most time in prison and could be avoided by betraying the other prisoner. In fact, the options could be analysed further – if the prisoner stays silent, either they go to prison for 1 year, or 3 years. If the two options had a 50% chance each of happening, this would mean that the average time spent in jail for staying silent would be 2 years, while if the prisoner was to talk the average would be just 1 year in jail. Therefore both prisoners would be playing smart if they betray each other. So what we find is that if each prisoner tries to achieve an optimal result for themselves, they arrive at the result which is least optimal for the both of them. Such a situation is referred to as a Nash equilibrium – a situation where no player in a game has any reason to change tactic, even though the result may not be optimal. The concept of the Nash equilibrium will be central to our understanding of Braess' paradox.

While being stuck in traffic may feel like being in prison, the example of the prisoner's dilemma is not entirely fitting to road traffic. It is hard to be emotionless in the prisoner scenario, because as humans we have notions of loyalty and betrayal that make the example shocking – especially if we consider that the prisoners may be imprisoned under an oppressive regime and therefore be imprisoned for some actions that would not be otherwise considered immoral. Traffic problems are plagued by selfishness, but no one believes in any driver having some sort of loyalty to other drivers in their vicinity. While actions of drivers can directly impact others, it is almost considered fair game to try to minimise your own travel time within reason. I say *within reason*, because some travel-optimising techniques can be dangerous, for example with frequent swerving between motorway lanes to get a short distance ahead. Most drivers are righteously angered by dangerous driving, as their lives may have been put at risk for little to no gain for anyone. Another difference is that in the prisoner's dilemma, the players know the effects on the others, while in road traffic scenarios, figuring out the effects of one's route choices on other drivers is almost impossible, especially while in the driver's seat.

The equivalent to Nash' equilibrium in transport is *Wardrop's Equilibrium*. This is where the journey times on all routes actually used are equal, and less than those which would be experienced by a single vehicle on any unused road[3]. A congested network in a Wardrop equilibrium will be such that no individual trip maker will be able to reduce his or her path by switching routes. Extended to scenarios where there may be different kinds of costs specified that may affect route choice, Wardrop's equilibrium would refer to a scenario where all routes used between an origin-destination pair would have equal and minimum costs while all unused routes have equal or greater costs. It is worth keeping these concepts in mind, as they will be central to understanding Braess' paradox.

---

[3]Modelling Transport, Ortuzár and Willumsen p. 367

To describe the scenario of Braess' paradox, some shorthand notation will need to be used to try and make it clear what is being discussed. The letters with an arrow over the top will refer to a path taken by a vehicle through the points that are labelled with the letters. So $\overrightarrow{ab}$ will refer to a path taken by a vehicle through points a and b. $\overrightarrow{abc}$ would refer to a path going through points a, b, and c. This notation with a subscript t will refer to the average time taken to go through that route. So $\overrightarrow{ab_t}$ will refer to the average time it takes for a vehicle to go from a to b. $\overrightarrow{abc_t}$ will refer to the average time it takes for a vehicle to travel from a to c via some intermediate point b.

Let us now consider a simple network where there are two roads going from point a to point z. The first road passes through the intermediate point b and the second road passes through intermediate point c.

We will set the times taken to travel on the associated routes to be defined in seconds as:

$$\overrightarrow{ab_t} = \overrightarrow{cz_t} = 10\psi$$

$$\overrightarrow{ac_t} = \overrightarrow{bz_t} = 100 + \psi$$

Where ψ is the number of vehicles travelling on that road.

Now in the case where there are say, 10 vehicles on this road, if they are initially evenly split between vehicles travelling from a to z via b and vehicles travelling from a to z via c, we find that each vehicle's time taken to travel the distance takes $10(5) + 100 + (5) = 155s$ (since they either travel via $\overrightarrow{ab}$ and $\overrightarrow{bz}$ or $\overrightarrow{ac}$ and $\overrightarrow{cz}$). They are in an optimal Nash equilibrium, since if a vehicle changed route, it would increase both its own travel time and that of the other vehicles in the network. Say if a

Figure 2.2: Two roads go from point a to point z, one via b and one via c.

vehicle switched from travelling via b to travelling via c, we would now have 4 vehicles taking 144 seconds and 6 vehicles taking 166 seconds, with a travel time average of $(144 \times 4 + 166 \times 6) \div 10 = 157.2s$. Therefore all the drivers are encouraged to optimise the network through the fact that they will decrease their own travel time by travelling down the less busy road.

Now if a new road is opened between b and c with a new travel time equation of:

$$\overrightarrow{bc_t} = 10 + \mu$$

We find that the dynamics of the network will change entirely.

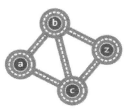

Figure 2.3: A new road is added between b and c that can provide a shortcut.

If a driver who would normally travel via b now decides to change his route to go from a to b,and then to c, before finally going to z, their journey time will now only take $10(5)+10+(1)+10(6) = 121s$, an improvement of 34 seconds. Note that the second 10 was multiplied by 6, as the road from c to z will now have an additional driver on it. The drivers still taking their normal routes will also have changed travel times. Those travelling along the road $\overrightarrow{abz}$ will now take $10(5)+100+(4) = 154s$ and those travelling along the road $\overrightarrow{acz}$ will now take $100+(5)+10(6) = 165s$ for a total average time of $(144 \times 4 + 165 \times 5 + 126 \times 1) \div 10 = 156.2s$. So the average time of all the vehicles has become worse.

As more cars discover this new faster road, matters will get worse. If a driver on road $\overrightarrow{abz}$ now switched to take route $\overrightarrow{abcz}$, the route $\overrightarrow{abcz}$ will now slow down to 132 seconds, while $\overrightarrow{abz}$ and $\overrightarrow{acz}$ will both take 164 seconds for an average time of $157.6s$. At the point at which there will be 2 vehicles left on each of $\overrightarrow{abz}$ and $\overrightarrow{acz}$, their travel times will have become 182 seconds, and route $\overrightarrow{abcz}$ will have slowed down to 176 seconds for an average time of 178.4 seconds due to the 6 drivers on its route - slower than the initial average by 23.4 seconds. At this point, none of the drivers would benefit by switching to a different route. If a driver on $\overrightarrow{abz}$ or $\overrightarrow{acz}$ switched to $\overrightarrow{abcz}$, their journey would slow down by 5 seconds, while drivers on $\overrightarrow{abcz}$ are already on the fastest route, so it would make no sense for them to change it. Clearly, they have reached a new Nash equilibrium and they have made their lives worse for it.

Every time that one of the drivers that would take the longest time to travel switches to a route that would take less time to travel on, they increase the amount of time it takes to travel on the other two routes. In fact the only route that has a temporary improvement in travel time is the route from which they are switching. The drivers on the routes $\overrightarrow{abz}$ and $\overrightarrow{acz}$ vie to not have the slowest route by switching to the route $\overrightarrow{abcz}$

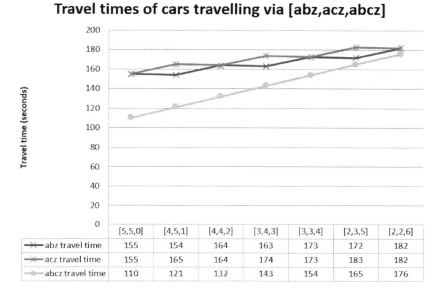

Figure 2.4: As the number of drivers taking the route *abcz* increases, the average vehicles on all the different routes increase until they reach an equilibrium where no change in route can improve a driver's journey time.

and thus slow the network down as a whole.

As single drivers travelling on the road with the longest travel time switch to route $\overrightarrow{abcz}$, both the minimum travel time and the total average travel times increase. Every single driver that tries to improve their travel time has made the travel times on this network worse as a whole.

While this may seem like quite a contrived problem that may have been invented by some mathematicians, the reverse has been found to be true. In 1983, while studying a random sample of road additions, Steinberg and Zangwill found that Braess' paradox could occur in almost half of the cases[4].

---

[4]Steinberg, R. & Zangwill, W.I. (1983), The Prevalence of Braess' Paradox. Transportation Science, Vol. 17, No. 3, pp.301-318

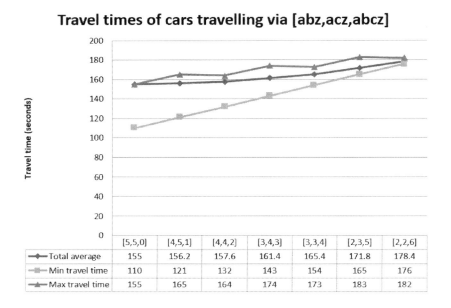

Travel times of cars travelling via [abz,acz,abcz]

	[5,5,0]	[4,5,1]	[4,4,2]	[3,4,3]	[3,3,4]	[2,3,5]	[2,2,6]
Total average	155	156.2	157.6	161.4	165.4	171.8	178.4
Min travel time	110	121	132	143	154	165	176
Max travel time	155	165	164	174	173	183	182

Figure 2.5: Here we can see the actual minimum, maximum and average times increasing as drivers switch to the route *abcz*, until the 3 times converge at the equilibrium.

So it has been ascertained that optimisations of individual journeys can have a negative impact on travel times within a traffic network and that opening a new road can also make traffic worse in various scenarios. From the perspective of transport authorities, it should then be clear that considerable effort should be put into deciding whether the opening of a new road will not have negative consequences of a network. Such decisions require considerable study, both from a perspective of the local road network and the wider network in that area. Such studies could be complex and costly – an authority would need to monitor the roads in the area under various traffic loads to figure out some equation for how the road behaves under varied amounts of vehicles on it. Then they would need to build models of the surrounding traffic network and hire an expert with the required mathematical skills to figure out what the

Nash equilibriums for the network are. The other problem for transport authorities is that there are probably innumerable cases of local road networks that have already reached sub-optimal Nash equilibriums. The users of these networks would all benefit from some method of ensuring they collaborate to optimise the travel times for all the drivers as a group, sacrificing their individual travel time optimisations. How could such collaboration be achieved?

There are various options for trying to optimise roads in these scenarios, some of which are more invasive than others. The most straightforward answer would be to close problematic roads down. This is certainly a possibility in certain areas where the roads are not essential to the area. However, there may be residents and businesses on the road that would not want such a closure. A partial closure of the road – such as closing it on one end is a viable middle ground, but it may still not be desired by the local community. A closure on one end of the road might mean that travelling to the other side of that closure might take a long time, as there may not be another simple route in that direction nearby.

Another option would be to make it less desirable to go down such a road – either through bringing in speed bumps, lower speed limits, or putting some form of toll on the road. Tolls could use automatic number plate recognition (ANPR) in order to not slow the traffic down, but still charge drivers going down such a route. They could be free for residents and local businesses, ensuring they have local support. However, there would be quite a few technical problems with bringing in a lot of tolled roads across urban areas. Authorities would have to make it clear which roads are tolled, and how much they cost. It could be hard to put sufficient signposting around certain roads that were to be tolled and if they were not sufficiently signposted, any charges levied upon drivers would be unfair and could be appealed against.

The problem with any scenarios that decrease the appeal of certain roads is that they do not necessarily solve the problem of reaching a sub-optimal Nash equilibrium. In our previous example of routes going from a to z, we can consider techniques that would try to discourage drivers from using the road from b to c. We can assume that drivers have some form of distribution of tolerances of the various annoyances (speed bumps or tolls). Some drivers are happier than others to drive over more uncomfortable speed bumps or pay higher tolls in order to reach their destination faster. If the annoyances are below a threshold that actually dissuades any drivers from taking that route, all that has happened is that there is no improvement in the traffic network, and drivers just face a higher average level of annoyance in crossing the network. If the annoyances are at such a level that they would stop some of the drivers from taking that route there will be marked improvement, but unless the annoyance is such that no drivers will take the route, the network will still be sub-optimal. Bringing in such annoyances can also make drivers annoyed, obviously. Drivers may feel that the social benefit may not be quite justified and that they should be allowed to go down this route. A case for such a position would especially be clear if this network only has 10 cars on it during peak hours. There may be times where there is only 1 car on the route, and the driver would have been slowed down by the decision to make the route bc annoying to travel on. Conditional rules could be added for the case of tolling – such as allowing traffic to pass through the road for free during off-peak times, but this would make signposting and notifying the drivers of the toll rates even more difficult.

If roads were to be filled with publicly owned driverless cars, road tax could be changed entirely. People would be picked up by cars from their origin and taken to their destination. They could be charged according to some function of the distance they wish to travel and how socially optimal a route they want to take. The public ownership of such vehicles would allow complex calculations to be performed, deciding what the charge should be for various routes, taking into account their current traffic levels and whether the choice of those routes could have negative impacts on other vehicles. Some people might see a problem with such a situation, due to the fact that it would mean that the rich could afford to travel via routes that are optimal for them, making the poor suffer for it, as their routes will get worse by the choices of the rich. Such a problem could lead to an even greater rift between the rich and the poor. There are potentially ways that this problem could be healed though. Prices could increase exponentially according to the level of social damage a problem does, and part of the charge could be reinvested in those affected. The higher tax of those taking problematic routes could be used to decrease the costs of those travelling on the socially advantageous routes. The subsidies for the travel of those who are socially minded should balance out their discomfort of taking a potentially longer route.

Unfortunately we are not yet at the stage where we have a large amount of publicly owned driverless cars in cities, and we may not be at that stage for decades or centuries. A similar tax could of course be applied without driverless cars, but drivers would have to be constantly fed travel information to help them decide which routes to take. Drivers would have to pay attention both to their driving and the costs they would incur on various roads. Both this and the previous scheme would be rather invasive, especially in terms of privacy of the people. Authorities would have to know where people travelled in order to be able to charge them for their journeys accordingly. Currently vehicle monitoring is not very invasive in this respect and a sudden increase in such monitoring could lack public support. An ability of authorities to track where everyone travelled on roads would also be incredibly dangerous if the authorities ever became tyrannical. Arguments could be made that authorities already more or less have such knowledge on public transport, but an acknowledgement should be made of the fact that private vehicle travel has always meant additional freedoms and privacy, which is what many people love about this form of transport. Authorities should be limited in how many restrictions they can put on freedom and privacy and so far, a good balance has been found with how roads are monitored. It may be unwise to press for further restrictions.

A less invasive way of trying to approach the problem would be to push for existing navigation technology to have features where users can choose to have the software pick socially optimal routes instead of the fastest routes. Such a scheme would rely on people's good will, but it would be certain to improve the situation, even if it wouldn't be as noticeable as if it was enforced by authorities. Local authorities modelling traffic scenarios would probably have to offer open data as to traffic preferences in the area, and such a scheme could be started at local levels before it is more broadly approached in the wider world. The freedoms of vehicle owners would be preserved, but good will could also be promoted to encourage people to do what was best for people in their area. It would be impossible to force people into using socially optimal routes in this way, as even if most navigation technologies took on data as to which roads were more optimal, another company could offer an alternative technology that gets people faster to their destination. No doubt someone would always buy into such an option, but hopefully at least a large part of society would be interested in working together to help each other.

While there is clear evidence that Braess' paradox is in play, actively seeking out cases of the paradox and solving the situations are not a part of authorities' typical operation. When managing traffic, transport authorities will look at areas that are problematic with regards to traffic, rather than necessarily trying to optimise every part of the network[5]. This is only natural, as traffic network complexities are immense and optimisations for one sub-network can be suboptimal for other sub-networks. Authorities may also have other priorities – for example, local Authorities in London interact with GPS navigation companies like Waze to make sure the software does not send drivers down roads with schools or other buildings that should only really have traffic access for those that need the services provided there. The concept of routing designed with the *greater good* in mind is already in play, but it is not solely driven by traffic flow optimisations. New emerging technologies, such as Transport for London's Surface Intelligent Transport Systems have further ambitious goals, such as changing driver behaviour in such a way as to improve both traffic and pollution.

Many future technologies are being designed to be led by simulation. When faced with some form of disruption, authorities would like to be able to immediately simulate a few responses to the disruption to see which one is likely to have better results for the surrounding network. There will only be one chance to affect the outcome of any disruption,

---

[5]Unlike academics, who may be doing all sorts of strange things, such as researching road planning strategies using slime mould [Andrew Adamatzky, Jeff Jones Road planning with slime mould: If Physarum built motorways it would route M6/M74 through Newcastle (2009)]

so running a few simulations and comparing results can help inform a critical decision. Authorities would also like to test the results of certain strategies after they have happened, to try to understand what-if scenarios for other strategies that could have been tried. With technologies such as these, an operator does not have to think about the intricate mathematical details involved in understanding what is happening in a network. Instead, comparisons can be made between scenarios and then a strategy can be chosen appropriately. Problems such as Braess' paradox will show up in such simulations and the effects can be compared with other options, allowing the operators to improve the situation. Authorities need to be careful with how they approach forecasting models and simulations. The 1960s and 70s resulted often in cases where too much time was devoted to developing models rather than testing alternative policies. Transport planners were often too occupied with the technical problems of their models, rather than with the transport needs of the community at large[6]. There is currently a modern line of thought that maybe increased computing power and availability of machine learning techniques will solve many of the problems faced back in the 70s, but certainly planners should still be wary of getting too caught up in their simulations.

Optimisations for a certain situation on a network can also be sub-optimal for other situations. In the scenario we discussed before where Braess' paradox occurs, the network is actually vastly improved with the additional road when there are 5 or fewer cars. Even with 6 cars only one vehicle would need to travel on one of the slower routes to socially optimise that network. Transport authorities therefore are inclined to deal

---

[6]David Boyce and Huw Williams, Forecasting Urban Travel (2015, Edward Elgar Publishing) p.122.

with traffic situations responsively rather than proactively – situations that are ongoing problems have to be improved, but improving hypothetical scenarios could make the situation worse for networks at the capacities they are operating at most frequently. Since traffic networks can be optimised for different traffic capacities, this means that traffic planning and management is highly political if thought about carefully – different people will certainly care whether the network is improved for those travelling during rush hour or for those that use the network when working or commuting during the day.

2.3 Lewis-Mogridge Position

The previous section made it clear that additional roads can have a negative impact on a local network. But could the impact on the broader network be more positive? In 1990, two transport workers by the names of David Lewis and Martin J. H. Mogridge brought us further bad news. The Lewis-Mogridge position observes that traffic eventually fills up new roads, ending any potential temporary advantage they could bring to traffic. The principles behind it are in fact a bit simpler than that of Braess' paradox. When more roads are built, more people are encouraged to travel by road, due to the supposed improvement of the road networks. Lewis and Mogridge observed that the roads can in fact fill up within weeks, nullifying any positive impact expansions could have had. It could be argued that the expansion would have benefitted those people who have now decided to use these roads, even though the network hasn't become better for any additional drivers who may want to switch to road. However, it should be noted that the intention of expansions can be to aid the traffic on the current roads. In those cases, the Lewis-

Mogridge position postulates that the solution can only be temporary, unless there was a possibility of infinite expansion.

More worryingly, the Lewis-Mogridge position can have an additional negative impact when it is combined with poorly designed networks. The effect of Braess' paradox can be exacerbated if a new road also comes attached with new vehicles. Looking at the example we studied in the previous chapter, if the additional road $\overrightarrow{abcz}$ meant that an additional 2 drivers joined the network, the Nash equilibrium that would be reached would be even worse.

In this scenario, at first there are 5 vehicles travelling on each of $\overrightarrow{abz}$ and $\overrightarrow{acz}$. When $\overrightarrow{abcz}$ is built, 2 new additional vehicles (probably locals who heard about this new road first) fill this road before any of the other vehicles start switching. After this addition, the vehicles that had driven on the network for a long time suddenly notice that there is a faster route on their network and start switching to $\overrightarrow{abcz}$. We find that the eventual transit time gets much worse than previously (193 or 196s instead of 182 or 176s).

The Lewis-Mogridge position logically results in an attitude that dictates that road additions are not worthwhile and that instead it is more important to manage the traffic that is already there on the network, trying to improve it without encouraging more vehicles to travel on it.

2.4   Downs-Thomson Paradox

To make things even more complex, it turns out that transport in cities can be in an even wider Nash equilibrium. If a city has the vast majority of commuters travelling by rapid transport systems, it turns out that the speed of car traffic becomes linked to how well the public transport is

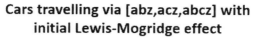

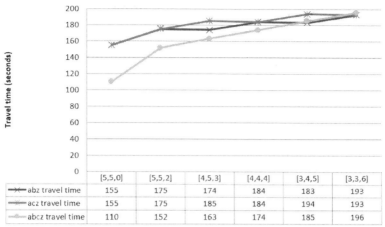

	[5,5,0]	[5,5,2]	[4,5,3]	[4,4,4]	[3,4,5]	[3,3,6]
abz travel time	155	175	174	184	183	193
acz travel time	155	175	185	184	194	193
abcz travel time	110	152	163	174	185	196

Figure 2.6: The Lewis-Mogridge effect states that when new roads are built, traffic will quickly fill up the new road. With new cars entering the network due to the addition of the road, the traffic gets worse, and it gets worse quicker for our scenario than just via the Braess paradox itself.

performing. The Downs-Thomson paradox states that in such cities, the equilibrium speed of car traffic is determined by the average speed of the public transport door-to-door equivalent. This means that if a road network is expanded, traffic will be added to it until the point where the option to go by car is no faster than travelling the same distance by public transport. This should make sense – as many people may decide to drive if it is faster than public transport, but would have less incentive to do so if it would be similar or slower.

The Downs-Thomson paradox tells us that in big cities, expanding the road networks will have little benefit for improving travel speed. It could still mean greater traffic flow in some cases, but travel speeds will not decrease by such an investment. Instead, if authorities invest in public transport and decrease the time in which people can get between two points by taking trains and buses, road users will naturally decrease in number and eventually reach the faster equilibrium. So this concept suggests that travel times will decrease the most if investments go into public transport, rather than road expansions for cars. However, even though investments into road networks may not improve traffic speeds, they may improve traffic flow, so may still be worthwhile. But together with the previous concepts we have learnt, the prospect of road traffic improving with road extensions seems worse and worse.

2.5   Improving Junction Traffic Flow

Some of the biggest contributors to slowing down traffic on roads are junctions. Whenever two or more roads cross, delays can occur for vehicles coming from at least one of the directions. How authorities design junctions can therefore have a major impact on the traffic on the roads attached to the junctions.

The simplest scenario for a junction is that of a T junction. When designing a T junction, it is important to consider which of the roads are more likely to have traffic on them and therefore what their order of precedence is. If two of the three adjoining roads are far more likely to have traffic than the third road, authorities will usually consider that the actual road. The third road will have give-way lines and vehicles travelling on that road will have to wait for sufficient space on the other two roads before they can proceed from this junction. The least busy road will therefore have the longest wait times, but such a scenario should affect the least amount of drivers, since this was the road with the least amount of traffic. Unfortunately, this can mean a large build-up of traffic on the usually least busy road if all three roads are busy at a particular time.

If the main road in this situation becomes too busy, the junction can be fitted with traffic lights, which would allow each road to periodically be given right of way and therefore ensuring everyone gets a chance to travel through the junction. In the case where the main road may be too busy for vehicles on the side road to have much of a chance to enter the main road via the junction but the road doesn't have traffic on it very often, sensors can be fitted on the traffic lights. The sensors will only allow the traffic lights to change if there are any vehicles on the side road, otherwise the traffic on the busier roads will remain unaffected.

If all three roads are similarly busy, it is hard to decide which roads should take precedence. In such a case, the concept of precedence can be removed and the junction can be given a roundabout. The roundabout will mean that all three roads would hypothetically have equal precedence over who can navigate the junction. I say *hypothetically*, because there will always be an imbalance if two of the roads are closer together or there is particularly a clearer view between two roads. In such a case, a particular road may be found to give way to drivers from another road more often. Either way, vehicles will go onto the junction whenever they see sufficient space on the roundabout. Therefore, there should be a constant stream of vehicles passing through the junction.

Junctions become more complex when they are the intersection of one or more main roads. Additional options are available in designing more complex and bigger junctions. For example, if there is an intersection of two main roads with four lanes each, the lanes on the driving side can be given a slip road into the roads turning in that direction[7],

---

[7]So, in countries where you drive on the left, slip lanes can be provided into turns going

meaning that vehicles turning in that direction will never need to stop at the junction. Vehicles continuing on a straight path or turning right will still need to consider a subset of the junction in the middle, which could either be a set of traffic lights or a roundabout of some sort. Further variations of junction types can be used in combination to achieve better traffic flows for roads of different traffic levels and sizes[8].

2.6 Vehicle Safety on Junctions

Vehicle safety is a very broad subject that can be approached from various conflicting perspectives. For example, the need to improve the safety of the driver and passengers can conflict with the need for the safety of pedestrians who may be hit by a car. There are also many different factors that can affect the safety of vehicles. The first and most obvious factor is that of speed. In the most simple scenario, of travel in a straight line with no interference of other vehicles (i.e. that of a train on a rail), safety is found to be proportional to the inverse of the speed of the vehicle[9]. The safety of Road vehicles, which have more degrees of freedom than trains, similarly has a strong relationship with speed. The risk of

---

left (e.g. UK). In countries where you drive on the right, slip lanes can be provided into rightward roads. The language of this book has become rather complicated due to my attempt to write for more generic scenarios.

[8]The YouTube user euverus has published an excellent video on modelling traffic flow across different types of junctions. It is definitely well worth a watch: https://www.youtube.com/watch?v=yITr127KZtQ

[9]As can be seen in Schlingensiepen, Nemtanu and Marinov's essay Systematic and Customer Driven Approach to Cost-Efficiently Improving Interlocking and SIgnaling in Train Transport taken from Rail Transport –Systems Approach p.249.

accidents occuring increases with the mean speed of vehicles[10][11][12], but it also increases as the square of the proportion of a vehicle's speed to the average road speed[13]. This means that those who travel faster than those around them on a road increase the risk of collision by a large factor.

In fact, driving at 10-20% above the average speed on a road increases the risk of a collision by the same amount as driving at the drink-driving limit[14]. As vehicles travel at higher speeds, the chances that a collision with a pedestrian will result in a severe injury or death drastically increases[15]. The chances of severe injury of passengers of vehicles increases with the power of three of speed and the chance of death of passengers increases with the power of four[16].

An interesting problem is that drivers do not have a way of knowing their own risk[17]. Drivers who speed may consider that their driving is

[10]D J Finch, P Kompfner, C R Lockwood and G Maycock, Speed, Speed Limits and Accidents, Transport Research Laboratory 1994.

[11]M C Taylor, D A Lynam and A Baruya, The effects of drivers' speed on the frequency of road accidents, Transport Research Laboratory 2000.

[12]Aarts, L.T., and van Schagen, I. 2006. Driving speed and the risk of road crashes: A review. From Accident Analysis and Prevention, 38(2), 215-224.

[13]It is worth reading the European Commission's article on speed and accident risk https://road-safety.transport.ec.europa.eu/system/files/2021-07/ersosynthesis2018-speedspeedmanagement.pdf

[14]Kloeden, C. N., McLean, A. J., Moore, V. M. & Ponte, G. (1997) Travelling speed and the rate of crash involvement. Volume 1: findings. Report No. CR 172. Federal Office of Road Safety FORS, Canberra

[15]Tefft, B.C. (2011). Impact Speed and a Pedestrian's Risk of Severe Injury or Death. AAA Foundation for Traffic Safety.

[16]Nilsson, G. (1982) The effects of speed limits on traffic crashes in Sweden. In: Proceedings of the international symposium on the effects of speed limits on traffic crashes and fuel consumption, Dublin. Organisation for Economy, Co-operation, and Development (OECD), Paris

[17]Notably, an analysis has found that vehicles were averaging 61mph in a dense fog, where the reasonably safe speed would have been 30mph [MacCarley, C.A., Ackles, C.,

safe, especially if they have not had an accident due to their speeding.

Psychologists note that while many people may consider that they try to drive as safely as possible, that is not the actual case. Rather than minimising their risk, drivers may actually maintain a subjectively optimal level of tolerated risk[18]. This means that drivers will drive slower when they consider themselves at risk due to some obstacles, but will increase their speed to approach a similar level of risk when there are fewer obstacles. In psychology, this concept forms the Risk Homeostasis Theory[19]. The theory does a good job of explaining bizarre problems, such as why ABS brakes on taxis have not noticeably reduced the amount of accidents in general but have instead increased the amounts of accidents in wet weather[20]. This is due to the fact that people notice that ABS brakes grip the road better, so will drive faster and closer to the vehicles ahead, assuming they will always be able to brake harder to stop in time. Similarly, a Norwegian study found no difference in accident frequency between drivers with studded and normal tyres – because

---

and Watts, T. 2006. Highway traffic response to dynamic fog warning and speed advisory messages from Transportation Research Record, 1980, 95-104].

[18]Wilde, Gerald. (2006). The Theory of Risk Homeostasis: Implications for Safety and Health. Risk Analysis. 2. 209 - 225. 10.1111/j.1539-6924.1982.tb01384.x.

[19]Like any scientific theory, it of course has varied academic support and opposition. RHT's most substantial criticism is that it doesn't easily allow scientific predictions to come from the theory. An offshoot of the theory that deals with this challenge is the Task Difficulty Homeostasis (TDH) theory, which matches drivers' ability to the task difficulties at hand, both of which allow methods that allow slightly more objective measurements, rather than the more elusive perceived risk. Other models, such as the Risk Allostasis Theory or the Multiple comfort zone model extend the concepts further. A highly recommended read on these topics is Christina M. Rudin-Brown and Samantha L. Jamson's Behavioural Adaptation and Road Safety

[20]Gerald J.S. Wilde Homeostasis Drives Behavioural Adaptation from Christina M. Rudin-Brown and Samantha L. Jamson's Behavioural Adaptation and Road Safety p.76

while drivers with normal tyres were taking particular care, drivers with studded winter tyres were merely allowing themselves to drive at higher speeds[21]. The added risk (and therefore slower speeds) as a result of changing from left-hand to right-hand traffic in Iceland in 1968 actually resulted in a reduction of accidents, before returning to normal just after 10 weeks.

However, speed is not the only factor that affects the safety of road users. A major factor is the amount of conflict points on the road. These are points on the road where a collision is likely, due to interaction between vehicles. On straight roads, conflict points are temporal – they exist at the point in time and space where cars are changing lanes. But conflict points have definite, fixed places in space at any junction in the road. These can be counted by drawing lines of all possible routes vehicles may be driving through a junction and counting the intersections of the lines. At each of these points, two drivers who have different aims in navigating through the junction are at risk of collision if they fail to notice each other, respond in a timely manner or manoeuvre correctly. A modern approach to improve junction safety is to try to minimise the conflict points of junctions, and therefore try to reduce the chances of accidents occurring at the junctions[22].

One of the great inventions that eliminate conflicting paths on junctions is the turbo roundabout. These roundabouts require the drivers to have selected their path through the roundabout before they reach it. This means that weaving between lanes is restricted and in a sim-

---

[21]Fosser, S. 1996 Studded or non-studded winter tyres: No significant difference in risk of accidents from Nordic Road and Transport Research, 1, 16.

[22]Minnesota Department of Transportation. Traffic Safety Fundamentals Handbook. Office of Traffic Engineering, Minnesota Department of Transportation: St. Paul, 2001.

ple 4-road scenario, 16 conflict points can be reduced to just $10^{23\,24}$. Turbo roundabouts have proved immensely popular in certain countries. At the time of writing, about 300 of them have been commissioned in the Netherlands and the Dutch government has even developed its own turbo roundabout design guidelines.

Figure 2.7: Turbo roundabouts decrease the amount of collision points and therefore should improve safety on a roundabout through decreasing the amount of places that accidents can occur. This image uses right-hand traffic for the benefit of non British readers.

The secret of the turbo roundabout is the space where vehicles enter the roundabout from adjoining roads. Vehicles entering the roundabout have only one lane of cars coming towards them, so they can only cross the path of one lane of cars. Similarly, the drivers are not able to switch lanes on the roundabout. By minimising the possibilities of collision, it

---

[23] An excellent case for turbo roundabouts is made on the turbo roundabout website http://www.turboroundabout.com/benefits.html

[24] For reference, a single carriageway crossroad has 32 conflict points. See the EU Mobility and Transport document describing various junction types here: https://ec.europa.eu/transport/road_safety/specialist/knowledge/road/getting_initial_safety_design_principles_right/junctions_en

is hoped that collisions will decrease themselves. Drivers certainly have fewer risks to manage, and if these are not removed to the point of letting the drivers become complacent, the life of a driver should become much easier.

2.7 Pedestrian Safety over Traffic Flow

Another consideration for junctions is how to allow pedestrians to get across them. This might be irrelevant on some rural junctions between motorways where there aren't going to be many pedestrians. However, a large part of junctions are in urban or suburban areas. In fact, when considering pedestrians, any section of road can start to be considered as a junction – a junction between vehicle and pedestrian traffic. Roads block the path of any natural walking route from one side of the road to the other. If there is no nearby crossing across a road for a pedestrian, it is very likely that they will try to cross the road at the point at which they come to the road. Therefore it is necessary to try to provide regularly occurring pedestrian crossings along a road to ensure the pedestrians do not pick a dangerous place to cross it.

Safety of people in public space is a primary concern for any good government. It is also important to remember that there were pedestrians before any vehicles started to appear. People who walk have a lower carbon footprint than those who drive and the act of walking itself has shown to be beneficial to both physical and mental health. It would be illogical to promote the use of vehicles instead of supporting pedestrians.

Keeping pedestrians safe around fast moving, heavy vehicles can be a challenge. Drivers are liable to make mistakes or drive poorly, but pedestrians can also act irrationally. It is usually legal for pedestrians to be drunk, for instance, which means that they can have a poor sense of balance, slow reflexes and poor awareness. Local authorities therefore often have to consider placing barriers between roads and entrances to drinking establishments. Traffic lights and zebra crossings are clearly marked so that pedestrians can't miss them and can be aware when they need to cross.

The responsibility of care at pedestrian crossings is then a slightly controversial topic. Some countries consider it is the driver's duty to ensure the driver does not hit a pedestrian, while other countries have placed laws that give pedestrians the responsibility to ensure they are not hit by a vehicle at a crossing.

There have been attempts at standardising traffic laws, such as with the Vienna Convention on Road Traffic. There were 78 parties to this convention, and 36 of the parties signed it. This convention suggests that pedestrians should use a pedestrian crossing, where one is available and should not cross a carriageway without exercising care. If a crossing is equipped with light signals, the pedestrians should obey the light signals. Otherwise, the pedestrians should not step on to the carriageway without taking the distance and speed of approaching vehicles into account[25]. However, the convention left room for interpretation by the signatories by stating that *Contracting Parties or subdivisions thereof may impose stricter requirements on pedestrians crossing the carriageway.*

The Vienna Road Traffic Convention also had some rules that should govern the behaviour of drivers towards Pedestrians[26]. The Convention

---

[25]Article 20, point 6 of the Vienna Road Traffic Convention 1968. Free to read online here: https://www.unece.org/fileadmin/DAM/trans/conventn/crt1968e.pdf

[26]But even some rules within the Vienna Convention have allowed for an amount of diversity that can confuse people. For example, it has been shown that a significant amount

tried to stop drivers from behaviour that could endanger pedestrians by enforcing the stopping at traffic light signals, ensuring that drivers drive slow enough near other types of crossings to not endanger pedestrians who may use them and prohibiting the obstruction of pedestrian crossings[27].

While the vast majority of the world's countries are not signatories of this convention, even the actual signatories have a varied approach to how drivers and pedestrians should interact. Most of the countries of Europe were signatories, but Europe has a large range of different traffic laws depending on which country you are in. For example, the UK bans pedestrians from motorways, but otherwise there are no laws preventing jaywalking (crossing a road that has traffic). British children are taught to *Stop, Look and Listen* when preparing to cross a road. The UK's Highway Code also states that a driver should *watch out for pedestrians crossing a road into which you are turning. If they have started to cross, they have priority, so give way.* This is in stark contrast to laws of other European signatories of the Vienna Road Traffic Convention.

Poland is a good example of another signatory state that has entirely different laws. Poland enforces laws that fine pedestrians 150PLN if they cross at a red light or if they cross the road within 100 metres of a traffic light but not at the traffic light itself[28]. In addition, a green light for

---

of drivers don't understand the variations of light signals at public road level crossings and are therefore at risk of collisions with trains [Basacik, Cynk, Flint, McMorrow What Does it All Mean? Road User Comprehension of Signs and Signals at Public Road Level Crossings from Dadashin, Scott, Wilson and Mills' Rail Human Factors: Supporting reliability, safety and cost reduction (2013) CRC Press, Taylor & Francis Group pp.35-44]

[27] Article 21 of the Vienna Road Traffic Convention 1968.

[28] In fact, the Polish government is unwilling to change these laws even though there are highly probably links to high rates of traffic accidents, injuries and deaths. See my interview with campaigner Stefan Tompson who has worked towards decriminalis-

pedestrians does not necessarily mean it is safe to cross in Poland. Many crossings are designed in such a way that cars can still travel through pedestrian crossings while the pedestrians are shown a green light. It is up to the pedestrians to ensure that there are no vehicles approaching the crossing before they cross, even though there is a green light. This is a very liberal interpretation of the Vienna Road Traffic Convention, which suggested that pedestrians should obey any traffic light signals available. But if pedestrians obeyed Polish traffic lights without further attention to road traffic, they could easily be hit by a car.

The ability to travel across the European Union freely without much obstruction means that pedestrians can easily travel to countries where traffic laws may vastly differ from the country they have originated in. If tourists do not study local pedestrian laws carefully before travelling, they can be endangered by things such as the fact that it may always be safe to cross on a green light in one country but not in another. Even if they are not endangered, they are liable to penalty fares that they may not have been aware of at the time.

A recent idea for improving pedestrian safety that has been tried recently in some countries is the concept of Shared Spaces. These are sections of road where anyone can use any mode of transport. The uncertainty of who has priority on these sections of the road is part of the aim of the design. The reasoning goes that if it is unclear who has priority, everyone will take additional care with ensuring that there are no collisions or accidents. Drivers are expected to reduce their speed a lot on Shared Spaces to deal with the higher risk of collision. All in all, the additional measures to deal with the uncertainties on Shared Spaces are

---

ing jaywalking and improving pedestrian safety in Poland for more details http://www.michalpaszkiewicz.co.uk/blog/jaywalking-poland/

hypothesised to increase pedestrian safety.

The safety of Shared Spaces is disputed, especially amongst disability campaign groups[29]. Most current designs for Shared Spaces include making it unclear where an area that is safe for pedestrians may begin. Therefore it can be dangerous for the blind, as they have no way of telling when they are safe and when they are at a point where they may be in the way of moving vehicles on such a road. Furthermore these designs do not have any form of markings that would make it clear for the blind that they are on a Shared Space rather than on the pavement of an ordinary road. Putting in features for the blind to help them realise they are on a Shared Space and that they are on a particular part of a Shared Space slowly moves the road away from the ambiguousness of a full-on Shared Space and more towards a traditional road with pavements. Middle grounds have been found with ideas such as the Urban Crop Circle, which is a design present on the road that can trick drivers into thinking there will be a roundabout when there isn't one. These circles are usually partially on the pavement, adding to the confusion. The hope is once again that the confusion will lead to greater care amongst drivers when trying to navigate a junction with this feature[30]. These features can be related back to the concept of risk homeostasis – which states that drivers react to perceived safety by taking more risks[31]. With the con-

---

[29]Lord Holmes' report from July 2015 also suggested that shared spaces are rather unpopular amongst most groups of people. Whether that is also a feature of the design is possibly a separate question. The report can be seen here: https://www.theihe.org/wp-content/uploads/2013/08/Holmes-Report-on-Shared-Space-.pdf

[30]99percentvisible have an excellent article on Urban Crop Circles available here: https://99percentinvisible.org/article/urban-crop-circle-ghost-roundabout-designed-confuse-slow-drivers/

[31]Risto Kulmala and Pirkko Rämä Definition of Behavioural Adaptation from Christina M. Rudin-Brown and Samantha L.Jamson's Behavioural Adaptation and Road Safety – The-

cept of risk homeostasis, the perceived risk of drivers will stay more or less constant over their journeys, as they adjust their driving to maintain their favoured level of risk. However, designs such as Urban Crop Circles can increase the perceived risk of a situation, making the driver take fewer risks, while not making the situation objectively riskier – meaning that while perceived risk has stayed constant, actual risk would have decreased considerably. Similar concepts have been used to encourage drivers to take extra care when approaching level crossings. Research in Israel showed that 90% of those crashing through lowered barriers at level crossings were surprised and most likely didn't pay enough attention on the road leading up to the level crossing[32]. The research found three different road design options to try and deal with the scenario:

1. Putting lines on the road with slowly decreasing distances between the lines, creating an illusion of high speed and encouraging further deceleration.

2. Slowly increasing the width of the lines painted on the sides of the road, creating an illusion of the road narrowing fast, increasing a feeling of risk

3. Introducing a *carpet* area leading up to the crossing, with a picture of a train on it, making the crossing more visible and explicitly labelled.

The results showed that the two illusions that increased the perceived

---

ory, Evidence and Action (2013) p.17

[32] Cale, Gellert, Katz and Sommer Can you tame a level crossing? Results from a driving simulator based paradigm from Dadashi, Scott, Wilson and Mills' Rail Human Factors: Supporting reliability, safety and cost reduction (2013) CRC Press, Taylor & Francis Group p.61

Figure 2.8: Lines with decreasing spacing make it feel like you are not slowing down as fast as you actually are, encouraging drivers to slow down more.

Figure 2.9: Making it seem as if the road is narrowing increases the feeling of risk and drivers slow down more.

danger resulted in vehicles slowing down the most on the approach to the level crossings.

While such ideas for encouraging behavioural adaptation may seem attractive, it is worrying to consider the possibility that a continued use of such techniques may eventually result in a desensitisation of the perceived risky situations (as the drivers would not be crashing and will

Figure 2.10: Very clear visibility of an upcoming risk should make drivers more aware from further away.

start seeing that the danger is not as great as they initially perceived), and may therefore increase their risk tolerance and become riskier drivers in the long run[33].

The Sustainable Safety principles are an alternative framework for safety in urban planning. These are almost entirely opposed to the ideas of Shared Spaces and Urban Crop Circles. There are four core principles:

1. Roads should have a single function. This concept splits roads into different functions – trunk, distributor and access roads. Trunk roads are supposed to move large volumes of traffic over greater distances. Access roads should take people to the houses, shops or other locales that people would like to travel to. Distributor roads are the roads linking trunk roads to the access roads. This idea means that roads that provide access to places people visit will not be full of fast moving traffic.

---

[33]Urban Crop Circles are too recent a design principle for considerably study to have been made into whether such worries of iatrogenesis are well founded.

2. Only modes of transport of the same mass, speed and direction should occupy a section of the road. This means making a clear separation between most modes of traffic – cyclists shouldn't share a space with pedestrians and cars shouldn't share a space with cyclists. The clear separation should make it easier to keep each lighter and slower mode of transport safe from the heavier and faster modes of transport.

3. Road designs should be instantly recognisable. When entering a road, it should be obvious what is expected of the person entering that road. It should be clear where a pedestrian can or should cross, where and how vehicles should drive, and it should be clear what the purpose of that road is (whether it is a Trunk, Distributor or Access road).

4. The environment should be forgiving. It is obvious that people make mistakes and this principle tries to bring this fact into the planning for that road – roads should be designed in such a way that a mistake of a person causes the least amount of damage or problems possible.

It should be pretty clear how Shared Spaces are in opposition with almost of these principles. Shared Spaces clearly do not split the road based on mass and speed, they do not make it clear what is expected of any particular mode of transport, and it is certainly not a forgiving environment – a mistake could easily lead to a collision between a vehicle and a pedestrian[34]. For the designers of shared spaces, these are in fact not errors of this kind of space, but a feature of them! The first princi-

---

[34]For a more detailed breakdown of https://aseasyasridingabike.wordpress.com/2017/11/22/sustainable-safety-and-shared-space/

ple might be met if the road is an access road, for example. However, many roads that have been turned into Shared Spaces do not meet it. For example, Exhibition Road in South Kensington is a road that both provides access to restaurant and museums, but it is also a convenient through road for large volumes of traffic and was certainly used by large quantities of vehicles before it was redesigned to be a Shared Space.

There are of course arguments against Sustainable Safety as well. The Sustainable Safety principles put the responsibility into the hands of the government - or a more local ruling authority – to minimise risks, injuries and deaths on roads.

One of the arguments against these principles is that they encourage people to think it is not their own responsibility to keep everyone safe when they are travelling. It is possible that people who are accustomed to roads where the safety is provided for them by the design of the roads may assume that the same safety has been provided in areas where it hasn't, meaning that they can become less careful than they should be on roads where the principles have not been put into practice. Some people would claim that this is not a valid argument and that clearly the solution to this problem would be to make ALL roads follow the Sustainable Safety principles so that such situations do not occur. This counter is clearly not pragmatic, as the cost of such development would be immense and probably could not be handled by most governments of major countries. Opponents of sustainable safety point to the fact that people have the capacity to travel down roads safety with mixed vehicles on the same road and that assuming that they can't is frankly patronising. If the need for the driver to be careful is diminished, will the safety of their driving also not diminish? Economist Gordon Tullock took this argument to its full conclusions and argued that cars could only be a fully safe form of transport if there was a spike installed on every steering wheel. Drivers would constantly be terrified for their lives and would therefore ensure their driving was safe at all times[35].

Having separate infrastructure for modes such as bicycles can also often be a poor use of space. The usage of bicycle infrastructure varies greatly with weather. When it rains, bicycle infrastructure may often not be put to use at all! While not being put to good use, bicycle infrastructure can also interfere with other traffic[36]. Infrastructure that may interfere while not being put to good use isn't a good idea, but it should be noted that it will not apply to all cases of bicycle infrastructure. Technical solutions are also available to help improve the usage of cycle infrastructure. Cycle lanes could be covered with a roof covered with plants, which could help the environment, form part of a green noise barrier, and encourage cycling in bad weather. Such a project could be very expensive, but if built correctly, it could last a long time and have many great benefits.

For the reader that is still hopeful that we may still be able to travel around faster in the future, it should be worth noting that Sustainable Safety, if implemented to the point where motor drivers never share road space with other modes of transport, should make it safe for higher

---

[35]There is clear evidence that increasing the cost of being at fault in an accident results in reductions of accident rates. For example, in Barmack and Payne's 1961 The Lackland accident countermeasure experiment (Highway Research Board Proceedings, 40, 513-522), military drivers were informed their ranks were in jeopardy and they ran the risk of dishonourable discharge from the service if they were found to be at fault in a road accident. As a result of these measures, the number of accidents diminished by 50%, the frequency of personal injury by 54% and the frequency of personal injury to the driver by 60%.

[36]Victoria Adams, Sudeeksha Murari, Christopher Round Biking and the Connected City 2017 (from Disrupting Mobility – Impacts of Sharing Economy and Innovative Transportation on Cities p.317)

speed limits to be allowed for motor vehicles. However, having such a great separation in the road space between the modes of transport is an exceptionally complex and expensive problem.

In conclusion we can see from this section that there are many different ideas of how we can approach safer roads. Some of these options are polar opposites of each other. No doubt the strategy taken by authorities will have a major impact on the traffic flow of people travelling via different modes of transport. It will also shape how people behave and will decide how pleasant it is to be on our roads.

2.8   Removing Parked Cars

Having a car gives a person a lot of freedom. It allows the person to at any point decide that they would like to travel and to take a pretty fast means of transport to get there without forward planning. The person can decide to take any route, be it the fastest or the most scenic and they can go alone or they can take some friends with them. However, the average car is disused and parked 96% of the time[37]. This means that the biggest collection of vehicles of any mode of transport is mostly not used for this transport. This is surely not efficient. However, there are further problems attached to this fact. Urban dwellers will certainly recognise the problem. Since there is an abundance of cars in cities (2.56 million cars in London, for example), they often take up a significant portion of the space on roads.

Many smaller or suburban roads often have both sides of the road

---

[37]In fact, the average car is parked 80% of the time at home and parked 16% of the time elsewhere. The average car is on the move only 4% of the time. This was found by an investigation by the RAC foundation in July 2012. https://www.racfoundation.org/research/mobility/spaced-out-perspectives-on-parking

lined with parked vehicles. These cars can make it difficult for cars to pass other cars that are travelling the other way down the road. Even on roads where the parked cars do not cause a problem for cars to pass each other, it is obvious that without the parked cars on either side of the road there could probably be an additional two lanes for vehicles to travel on. While it has been made clear earlier that adding lanes to roads only helps with traffic flow if the lanes are added over a stretch of road long enough for some people to get to their destinations, people who live in cities will probably be well aware that the vast majority of the road they travel on will have vehicles lining the pavement. There may not be parked cars on Motorways, but motorways are not usually the bottleneck on journeys, so a faster approach to a motorway would probably improve traffic flow in general. Those seeking to decrease the amount of parked cars do not always want to use the space created by removed parked cars for increased motor traffic flow. Some of them believe that this space would be better served by using it for aesthetic purposes – adding space for plants, popup shops or artwork.

How could all these cars be removed from the roads? One way would be to create more parking lots. These can use space more efficiently. They could also be underground and out of sight[38], making neighbourhoods more aesthetically pleasing, since parking lots can be an eyesore. Of

[38] Parking lots can also be mechanised. Mechanised systems store vehicles on shelves or conveyor belts and can allow 2-3 times as many vehicles to fit in the area of space they are using. Mechanised parking lots can also be much safer for the vehicles, which will be less likely to fall victim to theft or vandalism. The downsides are that they are more expensive to build (5X as expensive as raised parking lots for lots with ¡100 spaces, 3x as expensive for lots with 100-400 spaces and 2X as expensive for lots with ¿400 spaces) and require fast response times from engineers in the event of fault. For more reading on this topic, see Goel, Singh and Zhao's Underground Infrastructures: Planning, Design, and Construction (2012) Elsevier chapter 7, pp.103+

course, funding could otherwise be put into architecture and design of parking lots to make them look good even if they are not underground. Encouraging ride sharing[39] and public transport should theoretically help minimise the need for vehicles[40], but it is not clear whether that would result in fewer people buying and owning vehicles, or whether people would still own the same amount of cars, but keep them immobile for a greater proportion of the time.

The best way to help reduce the amount of cars would surely be to figure out a way to ensure that some form of public transport gives people the same freedom of mobility and privacy that they get with private cars. If this were to also be cheaper than the costs of buying, maintaining and fuelling a car, then that would surely be more attractive to most people.

Driverless car technology could be this solution. Driverless cars could be used highly efficiently – by being always on the move whenever they are not in need of refuelling. If these vehicles were to be electric, batteries could also be replaced in very small amounts of time, meaning that the vehicles could be on the move almost 24/7 if they needed to be. If

---

[39]Increasing ride sharing is a difficult problem in itself. One would think that altruistic reasons for ride-sharing should be enough to change driving culture, but academia suggests that financial motives have proved far more effective at encouraging ride-sharing, even if these are only a minimal income from renting vehicles or cutting petrol costs (Willhelms, Henkel, Merfeld You Are What You Share: Understanding Participation Motives in Peer-to Peer Carsharing, taken from Disrupting Mobility – Impacts of Sharing Economy and Innovative Transportation on Cities p. 106)

[40]Francesco Ciari and Henrik Becker, for example, found that ride sharing could decrease the amount of cars needed to complete nearly all car journeys by 75%. See essay How Disruptive Can Shared Mobility Be? A Scenario-Based Evaluation of Shared Mobility Systems Implemented at Large Scale (2017) available in the book Disrupting Mobility – Impacts of Sharing Economy and Innovative Transportation on Cities p.58.

driverless cars were to run a taxi-like service in cities, costs would also be noticeably lower, as the main cost of taxis is that of the driver's wages. At a very low cost, people could travel to anywhere with a high level of privacy, or if the right technology was available they could lower costs even further by sharing the driverless car with other people on their route. Companies running such services would also be keen to keep them on the move, meaning that it would be in the companies' interest to keep them efficient and therefore on the road, rather than parked. The lower costs should mean that the service would be more utilised than existing taxi or private hire services.

Some people clearly already believe in the vision, as seen by the fact that big private-hire companies like Uber are already making substantial investments in the technology[41] and are seemingly banking on the technology appearing soon, since their current profits are abysmal[42]. However, it is also not entirely clear whether self-driving cars will necessarily have a positive impact on society. Some models predict that driverless cars will be more attractive than current cars and may therefore lead to more people using driverless cars instead of public transport[43]. Such a shift could dramatically increase traffic on roads.

Whether the world will see a successful rollout of self-driving cars in the near future is however entirely moot. While the technology has been

---

[41] In 2018, Toyota signed a £500m deal funding Uber's driverless technology research programme, for example https://www.ft.com/content/1ca02574-aa2e-11e8-94bd-cba20d67390c

[42] Uber's revenue went up by 43% in 2018, but were still not making a profit (after almost a decade of annual losses) http://www.ejinsight.com/20190218-uber-revenue-up-43-in-2018-but-profit-remains-elusive/

[43] Bern Grush and John Niles, Transit Leap: A Deployment Path for Shared-Use Autonomous Vehicles that Supports Sustainability 2017. From Disrupting Mobility – Impacts of Sharing Economy and Innovative Transportation on Cities p.297.

trialled in many cities and towns and has shown vast improvements in a short span of time, it is still an incredibly tough problem to solve. There are also various levels of safety that can be met. These can be split into the following:

1. The safety of the average driver. Comparing safety statistics with all drivers is a bit flawed, in that very poor or aggressive drivers can skew the averages below par.

2. The safety of a good driver. If self-driving cars are to be seen to be *as good as humans* in terms of driving, they will have to be compared against a whittled down group of drivers who try their hardest to drive safely. Figuring out what this group would be as opposed to average drivers is a challenge in itself, as it has to be presumed that good drivers make some mistakes too, so it would be foolish to try to get statistics of drivers who have never been at fault for the accidents they are in, for example.

3. Faultless driving. Self-driving cars require cameras to drive safely, which means any incidents they are involved in are likely to be well documented. If at some point it can be shown that over the span of a few years (without removing the test vehicles on the roads) that no driverless cars were the causes of accidents and that they won all insurance cases, it will be clear that driverless vehicles are at this point performing better than their human counterparts and that if they replaced human drivers, roads would be safer.

4. Faultless defensive driving. The next stage in safety developments would be a situation where driverless vehicles do not cause accidents, but that they also reduce the amounts of accidents where

they are involved through another vehicle's faults. The concept of defensive driving is where the driver takes into account that the vehicles around the driver could also make mistakes and therefore preventative measures are taken to ensure this likelihood is decreased.

5. Absolute safety. The situation where self-driving cars are not involved in any accidents on roads. This would possibly be an impossible position to reach, but is obviously the naïve goal which any authority seeks.

The safety levels outlined would be a way of measuring how self-driving cars are progressing in terms of safety. However, the safety stage which governments take as acceptable for taking a decision of rolling out driverless vehicles is an entirely different question. It is doubtless that if stage 3 were to be met, there would be every reason to work towards increasing numbers of driverless cars – it would certainly reduce accidents and increase safety on the roads if there were more faultless vehicles. The difficult question would be around stage 2 – what statistics could be used to measure stage 2 and how much better would the driverless cars have to be in comparison to those statistics in order to make it a viable policy to push for driverless technology. This problem may become even more difficult as car companies develop technologies that can augment human driver safety. At the time of writing rear-view cameras, proximity sensors, speed limiters, and auto-stopping technologies are already widely used in the market. Will driverless cars have to compete with augmented drivers or with the drivers of the past when it comes to picking policies around driverless cars?

It is highly unlikely that driverless cars won't be rolled out eventually

– the fact that there are no limits on cameras that could be fitted, signals to be sent between vehicles, and the amount of computing that could be accessible mean that eventually these cars should be able to surpass human skill. But we cannot presume that this is going to be a problem solved quickly in any short-time scale. There are innumerable scenarios that can occur on roads. These need to be covered and tested against. Authorities that make policy on driverless technology would take partial responsibility over any accidents caused by these vehicles and therefore they are reluctant to proceed till strict controls can be ensured on the technology.

In terms of removing parked cars, the most interesting businesses in this respect will be technology companies that develop ways of retro fitting old cars with driverless technology – this would allow a clear way of putting currently immobile cars to efficient use. Owners of vehicles would see a clear benefit of letting their cars drive around and making money for their owners while they are off doing something else. Delegated ownership of cars would mean anyone could make profits through this system which should serve as a way to promote the driverless taxi scheme.

Of course, similar schemes have been tried with rentals – for example, Turo is a company that provides a means of peer-to-peer vehicle rentals and can already allow vehicle owners to make some money back and ensure their vehicle is being put to good use. Since such companies exist, it raises a question as to why most people aren't using this service already – are they not interested in renting out their cars and adding to their income, or are the companies providing this service just not well known enough yet? One way or another, a factor may remain – people like ownership and they can enjoy the fact that they own a particular vehicle. Renting out a vehicle to someone else who may damage it or even just dirty it make this prospect unappealing to many people. It seems then that even with the advent of driverless cars, peer-to-peer rentals may not be as popular as one would like and the parked car problem may continue to go unsolved without some other form of intervention.

It is plausible that an authority could try to bring in some additional tax on vehicles that are immobile most of the time, but adoption of such a policy would be difficult in many countries. Motoring associations and lobby groups are notoriously powerful and willing to fight such schemes. Vehicle collectors who may rarely drive some of their classic cars that they love to keep would be especially punished by a vehicle immobility tax. Such an immobility tax could also be seen as unfair, since even if suddenly most vehicles were put on the rental market, there would be far more vehicles on the rental market than people willing to rent them, meaning that the vast majority of people would be taxed due to the fact that they had been out-competed by other people with peer-to-peer rental vehicles on the market, meaning their loss in this competition would be double.

2.9 Platooning

An idea that has lately emerged thanks to the development of wireless technology is the idea that vehicles that are travelling on the same route can be linked in such a way that the acceleration and braking on a leading vehicle can trigger acceleration and braking on the vehicles behind. Such a technology can mean that provided that the vehicles have similar braking characteristics, they can travel much closer together (in platoons) as there would be almost no delay between the starts of the vehicles braking. This would mean that the traffic flow on the roads could be increased by improving vehicle technology and without a need for vast infrastructure developments on the roads. However, platooning has other more useful advantages. First of all, the close proximity of trucks can mean that a lot of energy is saved. Trucks face a large amount of air resistance while driving, due to the large surface area at their fronts. With multiple trucks in close succession, only the front vehicle would face the full effects of air resistance, since the vehicles behind would be in the slipstream of the lead vehicle. The vehicles behind would then require less force – and therefore less energy and less fuel – to travel to their destinations, meaning that the operation would both be less costly and better for the environment. The main reason that companies are showing interest in this technique though is due to the fact that it provides a means to put multiple vehicles in the control of a lead vehicle, meaning that theoretically there could be a single driver driving multiple trucks. Such a reduction in costs would be phenomenal for the freight industry.

Green Light Optimal Speed Advisory (GLOSA) is another technology that will mean a huge improvement in efficiencies for trucks[44]. The idea of this technology is that since road owners control traffic lights, they also know when they will change. They can use this information to advise drivers as to what (legal) speed is optimal to ensure that they reach the traffic lights when the traffic lights is green. Going any faster than such an advised speed would not help the driver in any way, as they would have to wait at a red light for the light to change. If the driver travels at the advised speed, they will not have to slow down at

---

[44]Bodenheimer et al. GLOSA for adaptive traffic lights: Methods and evaluation (2015) https://ieeexplore.ieee.org/document/7325247

the traffic lights, as they will be always reaching them on a green light. GLOSA is currently being trialled in the UK on the route from London to Dover and is a very promising technology. It will reduce pollution due to the fact that less energy is needed, since trucks will not have to accelerate and decelerate so much. Less fuel burnt means less greenhouse gases produced and released. GLOSA is also likely to encourage less aggressive and more stable driving which could be both safer and more pleasant for drivers on the road[45].

2.10 Changing the Vehicle Types

It has now been established that it seems there are few options with increasing traffic flow on already busy urban streets. One method we have not discussed yet is the idea of encouraging vehicles with a higher density of passengers onto the roads.

Traffic flow of people along a road can be modelled as the volume of people in a cross-section of the road multiplied by their speed travelling down the road. If there is some speed that the traffic cannot exceed, then the only factor that can improve that traffic flow is the density of people on that road. Cars have a very low density of people for the area of ground they cover, especially if the drivers have no passengers. Buses - especially double decker buses – and bicycles can vastly increase the density of people on a road. If road users were to take buses and bicycles, the traffic flow on roads could increase by a magnitude of 10! What is

---

[45] Although this may still not turn out to be entirely true. Some studies of similar technologies resulted in more stops and almost three times as many red light violations. See Marieke H. Martens' Behavioural Adaptation to Roadway Intelligent Transport Systems from Christina M. Rudin-Brown and Samanthat L. Jamson's Behavioural Adaptation and Road Safety p.146.

stopping everyone from switching over?

The case of the bicycle is fairly simple – some people can't ride bicycles, others don't want to work so hard when travelling. Many people travel too far to travel by bike, while some routes are just not feasible for bikes (such as a route that may require going on a motorway).

While bicycles may increase traffic flow when the traffic speed is constant, it is also clear that many routes will have speed limits that far exceed the speed that person could reach on a bicycle, meaning that this option would slow them down.

Does the traffic flow also lower when the commuters could drive on a motorway instead of taking a bicycle? Over 6 bicycles can fit into the space of most cars. However, when travelling at speed, cyclists will rarely cycle at such high density. If about 4 bicycles can take up the space of a car when travelling at high speed, to ensure they can actually improve traffic flow, they must be able to travel the route at least a sixth as fast as the car could. If a destination could be reached by a motorway in the UK (where cars can travel at 70mph), achieving a similar traffic flow via an alternative bicycle route would require the cyclist to travel at 17.5mph. UK's average cyclist's average speed is about 15.9mph[46] for men and 12.9mph for women. Surely in this case, traffic flow is higher with cars? We have not covered the whole picture here, though. To maintain a safe distance on motorways, drivers should remain 2 seconds behind the car in front. As cars travel faster, this distance increases. At 70mph, this distance equates to about 75 metres! Cyclists, at their highest speeds do not require quite as much space between them, because they usually can't travel fast enough to need such a big gap between

---

[46]https://www.cyclingweekly.com/fitness/training/13-ways-increase-average-cycling-speed-144937

them. Even with a low estimate now, where we expect say 20 cyclists to be able to fit in the space of a car and the 75 metres behind it, the speed at which the cyclists would need to go to maintain the same traffic flow would be 3.5mph. This is a walking pace. These cyclists could be much closer together and you could probably easily fit 100 cyclists in this space at this speed, meaning that the traffic flow would be 5 times as high. These 100 cyclists could probably also go quite a bit faster while still keeping their density, so the traffic flow would be much larger for the cyclists.

On top of this, Urban areas do not have many motorways and often have low speed limits that cyclists can reach, meaning that cycling in urban areas is a definite solution for increasing traffic flow. It is also healthy both physically and mentally (if one ignores the fact that the cyclist may be inhaling toxic fumes) and does not pollute the environment as much as motor vehicles. Why isn't everyone using bicycles? The reality is that few people have the interest in traffic flow that authorities do. Many people just want to get between two points as fast as possible in a convenient way, and bicycles can be seen as sub-optimal in both of these regards.

Making people switch to using buses instead of cars is a harder problem. Buses do not give the same amount of freedom – most people will not be able to travel door-to-door for their journey using one bus, and they certainly won't have the same privacy they would have had if they had taken a car instead. The use of buses as a method of increasing density of people on roads is also contrary to people's decision making process about choosing buses. People most enjoy taking buses when they are fairly empty - when it is easy to find a seat and when people aren't being crammed inside. So people enjoy taking buses most when the density of people is least. Obviously most buses that are even partially full have a higher density than cars, but there remains an opposition of people's desires to the increase of density on buses.

Authorities may also be inclined to decrease the amount of buses on a route if there are too few passengers. If the amount of people taking buses on a certain route could fit on 10 buses, but there are currently 30 buses on that route, why shouldn't the authority decrease the amount of buses there to make the service more efficient? But passengers may not like a scenario where buses are more packed and this decrease in the number of buses on this route may decrease the amount of people taking those buses. A decrease of people on these buses may once again trigger a further removal of buses and an endless cycle of bus removal may be met. Going the other way may also seem rather foolish – an authority may predict that people like rather empty buses, so they will add 10 more buses to a route. But it is difficult to say whether these buses will be filled in any certain amount of time and whether the investment will be worthwhile at all. Initially, the same people will probably be spread over this larger amount of buses. Small increments of additional buses could show little difference in the crowding of buses and may not be enough to encourage more people to take these buses.

It seems that transport authorities would do best if the populations they served enjoyed very cramped conditions on buses. If only every passenger was motivated solely by traffic flow instead of comfort and speed of transit! Unfortunately, most passengers do not like to be crushed while on public transport and would doubtlessly prefer more free space on buses. Could drivers be encouraged to take buses instead if buses were to become more comfortable? It is certainly possible, but it is not a strategy that is really being tried by transport authorities[47] – authorities are more interested in seeing how to fit more passengers onto a bus safely (although with maximum comfort for that capacity). Could a better strategy be to make buses more comfortable and to increase their numbers instead? The buses may also need to serve a larger variety of routes so that passengers are more likely to be able to find a combination of buses that takes them closer to where they need to go. So long as the buses have a higher density of passengers for the area of road they cover than cars do, the scheme would still be worthwhile – the traffic flow could certainly be increased. How much comfort could be allowed while keeping the service affordable is a different question and one that would have to be investigated. Private companies that may want to try to disrupt the market could attempt this approach without the need for the sponsorship of transport authorities, but company owners may see it as a high risk strategy, considering that it would be an entirely different approach to what most bus providers are doing.

2.11 Bus Lanes

Another option to try to promote buses is to give buses priority on roads. The opening of bus lanes is one way to achieve this. Bus lanes are an entire lane on roads where private vehicles are not permitted to drive. Having such a road available for buses would in theory decrease private traffic flow and improve travel times for buses. When people would see that buses are performing much better due to these lanes, they would be encouraged to take public transport instead of their own cars. Such

---

[47]I did travel recently on a double decker bus in Oxford that seemed to have a sofa upstairs, but the general quality of seats was not much better than on other buses.

schemes need to widespread to ensure that there are few points where buses in bus lanes may be stopped due to an area ahead that is a bottle-neck and does not have a bus lane.

However, bus lanes can be seen to be a bit hypocritical. If the problem that authorities are trying to solve is to increase the density of commuters on roads, then why are they decreasing the density of vehicles on roads by banning a large portion of vehicles from using one of the lanes? Certainly there are many sections of bus lanes that are often empty of vehicles while adjacent lanes may be full of cars. This strategy seems to be more of a long-term goal – get road users out of private vehicles and onto buses, and then increase the number of buses to handle the new amount of bus users. Eventually all bus lanes should be filled up with buses all the time and there will be no inefficiency due to the use of bus lanes.

In the meantime, there are many questions to be considered about the intermediate situation – for example, is it fair to fine cars that drive onto a bus lane, if there were no buses in the vicinity at all? The vehicle would clearly not be impeding on bus travel times. In fact, surely it is serving the authorities by increasing traffic flow? On the other hand, how could authorities enforce a private vehicle ban only in situations where these vehicles would block a bus? It could be done by comparing ANPR images with historical bus GPS data or by taking enforcement pictures from the buses themselves. However, a bigger problem would be the fact that many vehicles may be taking a gamble by taking a bus lane. There may be no buses around and the lane may seem empty. A driver may try to take this lane, but get blocked at some point further down the road for long enough for a bus to arrive and snap a picture that will result in a fine. Trying to solve such a problem would not be trivial.

A strategy that might be worth trying instead would be some form of signal-controlled bus lane that could act as a bus lane when buses are around, but authorities could give drivers clear direction that they can use it during times when there are no buses that can appear for a while.

Smart traffic lights – a similar concept - are now already used in many cities. These will turn green faster if there is a bus waiting at the lights. Such information can be gained either through using a GPS on the bus and notifying the traffic light that the bus is near, or by using vehicle recognition cameras that can tell if a bus is arriving.

3. *Why are transport timetables so inaccurate*

W HEN travelling, it is wonderful to have the ability to plan the journey ahead. Modern journey planning technology gives us an excellent method to do this and can provide us with various options. These options can be annotated with estimated lengths of time and even costs of journeys. It is then rather unfortunate that many journeys do not meet the plan. If the reason the journey didn't go according to plan is because of the commuter, it is understandable. But many journeys are delayed due to the transport systems themselves not running according to schedule. This section will explore why real transport systems may differ from schedule, what measures you can take as a consumer to deal with it and finally what changes in the future may improve transport scheduling.

3.1 Why Buses Come in Threes

One of the more typical problems with bus timetables is that buses are scheduled to arrive every few minutes, but instead it seems that there is always a long wait for a bus, followed by a number of buses that arrive in close succession[1]. Experienced commuters know well that the first bus will usually be full of passengers, while the one just behind it will be almost empty, meaning that it will usually be worthwhile to wait a little bit longer for a second bus.

This phenomenon is called *bus bunching* and can be caused by the slightest delay. When a single bus is slightly delayed[2], it will start taking on passengers that would have otherwise taken the bus behind. Additional passengers mean that there are increased loading and unloading times, as well as potentially more stops that the bus will have to stop at. These additional times mean the bus is delayed further and even more passengers start taking this bus than the one behind it. The bus behind is taking on fewer passengers, and therefore now has fewer delays and can travel faster. The situation spirals out of control and before anyone notices it, the bus behind has caught up to the delayed bus[3]. The people waiting for the delayed bus now have to wait much longer for their bus, and when it arrives, it is closely followed by a mostly empty bus. If there are two sets of buses bunched in a row, the delay between the first and the second set is likely to be even longer than if there was just one set of bunched buses.

How can this problem be solved? The solution is well known to au-

---

[1]It is well worth reading *Why Do Buses Come In Threes* by Rob Eastaway and Jeremy Wyndham, which also includes mathematical descriptions and solutions of more interesting problems, such as how fast one should run in rain to stay the most dry.

[2]And there will always be reasons for delays on public transport that will be entirely unavoidable. What marks a good operator is their ability to stop a single issue from making the whole service snowball out of control. See John Glover's Principles of Railway Operation (2013) Ian Allan Publishing p.17.

[3]There is an excellent interactive animation (http://setosa.io/bus/) that allows you to delay a bus ever so slightly and watch the chaos unfold. It is rather oddly satisfying.

thorities, but is not always so popular amongst passengers. To fix this problem, corrective measures have to be applied to the buses. Either the delayed bus should be sped up, by not allowing it to stop or take on additional passengers at stops, or the buses around the delayed bus need to be delayed a bit. If the bus in front is delayed, it will take on more passengers and relieve some of the stress on this bus. The bus behind should be delayed to keep a separation between the two buses, so that bunching doesn't happen once again behind the mostly-empty bus. In London, passengers in these situations are told that the bus is waiting in order to *regulate the service*. This is not always very popular amongst the commuters, as their journey is at this point being purposefully delayed – not something they expect from public transport.

Regulation of the service is an interesting topic, as it raises the question of who it is most important for transport authorities to appease – those who are waiting for their transport, or those who have already embarked on their journey and are inside their vehicle? By regulating the service, anyone in a bus being actively delayed loses out, as their journey would have been shorter if the authorities had not delayed it. If the service is not regulated however, buses could bunch and passengers may have to wait longer for buses and may not even be able to get on the first bus in a bunch due to the overcrowding. Even if reducing bus bunching improves some statistical figure, like the total average journey time of all passengers on that bus route, the intentional delay can be seen to intentionally target and reduce the quality of the journey of the people on that vehicle. No doubt the people on that vehicle may be angry. Meanwhile people waiting for a bus that has been regulated will likely not know that the bus that arrived quicker than it may have otherwise was due to some sort of regulation. This means that they may not feel any better about public transport than they would have otherwise. But is it not more important to provide an optimised and efficient service that provides the best quality service to the most people it can? But is it definitely *best quality service*, if some people are intentionally delayed?

There is of course another alternative, but as is the case with many alternative solutions it would be expensive. When a gap between buses grows, a bus that wasn't already on the bus route could be added to that bus route in that gap. The problem with this solution is that it requires a large amount of buses that are only there for dealing with this particular issue. There would have to be regular depots with buses that are waiting to fill growing gaps in bus routes. Why pay for buses and bus drivers that are likely to be waiting around without taking passengers? Such additional buses would have multiple benefits, though – not only would they improve the service and ensure that services are as good as the timetables given to customers (and therefore matching customers' expectations), but due to the fact that buses are most likely to be delayed when a particular route is busy for the bus route the buses would be inserted during busy times, reducing congestion on buses when it is most needed.

Could there be a possibility that the additional buses were to be put on routes when they are not busy and rerouted when a different bus route needed them? It could certainly be done, but the problem with this approach is that if the bus had picked up passengers, it wouldn't be a good service to those passengers to drop them off at a station before their final destination and driving off to somewhere else. What could be done is that buses could be rerouted at the end of their routes. Once a bus has dropped off passengers, there are no passengers on board that the bus would have to drop off. People may be waiting at the bus route end, but it would be likely that there would be fewer of them than in the middle of the bus route, and it would also not be as offensive to them to reroute that bus, as they had not boarded it and it could have rerouted for any number of reasons. Since it would be simplest and the least damaging to passengers to reroute buses at the end of routes, it would be wise to place our additional buses on short routes, where they finish their routes regularly and therefore can be quickly rerouted. But what happens if multiple of these buses get rerouted at short notice? Suddenly this short route starts to have a bad service, as multiple buses have been taken off it. The service on this short route would have to then be regulated, or it would become known as a route with a very irregular bus service.

With additional buses available, you can therefore decide to either increase the capacity on bus routes in your city, or you can increase the reliability of your timetables. Trying to do both is just a middle ground where you sacrifice one for another. If you try to have buses that are temporarily on bus routes, but their aim is to provide reliability, it inhibits their ability to react to reliability issues fast. What is more important to people, then? Is it better for passengers to have a reliable timetable, or to have more buses and therefore a greater capacity on a bus route? Opinions on this matter can differ according to many variables – not necessarily just personal preference. Where buses are sparse, a reliable timetable can be more important in order to plan a journey. In busy urban areas, a greater capacity can be far more necessary, as buses may already be struggling to pick up all the passengers waiting at stops.

It seems therefore that the most efficient solution remains the regulation of bus services. But this approach will require public understanding in order to not damage the bus providers' reputation in the eyes of passengers.

3.2 Average Wait Time for Buses

When waiting for a bus, a timetable typically displays that a bus should arrive either at some particular time, or every certain amount of minutes. If the bus should arrive every certain amount of minutes, we would expect the average waiting time for the next bus after an arrival to be half this amount. In reality however, it always seems we have to wait an extraordinary amount for a bus, never meeting our expectation of half the time between buses. Why does this happen?

In a perfect world, if buses were always arriving according to schedule, the average waiting time would indeed be half the time between the arrivals of buses (the bus headway). However, the moment a bit of inconsistency occurs on the bus route, we find that the average time passengers spend waiting increases. This is because of something called the inspection paradox.

The inspection paradox occurs when the probability of observing something is related to that observable. In the case of bus timetables, this means that when some buses are delayed, passengers are more likely to be waiting for a delayed bus, rather than the buses that are on time or early[4]. It will be easiest to explain this with an example.

Let us suppose that we have a bus route where buses arrive every 10 minutes. Every second bus becomes delayed by one minute (meaning that the other buses on the route now arrive a minute earlier than expected). If we look at a pair of buses, we can see that in a span of 20

---

[4]An excellent in depth article on bus waiting times is available here: http://jakevdp. github.io/blog/2018/09/13/waiting-time-paradox

minutes, there is one bus after 11 minutes and then a bus that arrives 9 minutes afterwards. The average arrival time of the buses is therefore still 10 minutes. What we find is that if a passenger was to arrive randomly at a bus stop on this bus route, the chance that the passenger would be waiting for the delayed bus is 11/20 and the chance of waiting for the early bus is 9/20. By multiplying the probabilities by the arrival times of the buses, we find that the expected arrival time of buses on this route is 11 x 11 / 20 + 9 x 9 / 20 = 10.1, and therefore the average waiting time would be 5.05, which is 3 seconds longer than what we would expect if the buses were running according to schedule. However, as the delay of the first bus increases, we find that the average waiting time increases proportionally with the square of the delay[5].

What is interesting about this result is that it could be used to measure how well buses on a route are keeping to a timetable. The difference between the average waiting time and the expected waiting time will increase exponentially with the difference between the timetable and live bus positions. If a particular bus is running early, it will make the bus behind it seemed delayed, as passengers will have to wait longer for it if they miss the early bus. Small differences between bus live and expected positions will make little difference to this score, while larger differences will be clearer, making it obvious if a bus service is performing particularly poorly with regards to the timetable. Gathering such data can be quite simple these days, especially in cities that offer bus arrival time data freely to the public.

---

[5]A good model for average passenger waiting time is given in Ortuzár and Willumsen's *Modelling Transport* as $\frac{h^2+\sigma^2}{2h}$ where h is the expected bus headway and *sigma* is the standard deviation of the buses from the headway. When the buses are running a perfect service, σ will be 0 and this equation will become $\frac{h}{2}$ as expected.

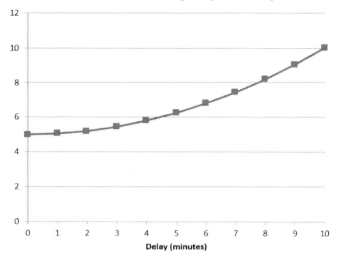

Figure 3.1: Given buses are supposed to be spaced 5 minutes apart, every minute the second bus is delayed behind the first leads to the y-axis amount of minutes of average delay time if a person arrives at random at the bus stop.

What stops authorities that find their buses always having large differences between average waiting times and expected waiting times from just changing their timetable? This is an interesting point and one that raises further questions.

I tried to find clear examples of the waiting time paradox in London by comparing live bus arrival times with the bus timetables[6]. On average, London buses were arriving quite a bit earlier than expected according to the timetable. The factor that most people don't think about is how the transport authorities are treating the bus timetable. Is it being generated by the authority post factum, letting people know what

---

[6]As can be found here http://www.michalpaszkiewicz.co.uk/blog/timetables/ with real-time data.

should be expected, or is the timetable set up for the authorities to try to meet?

It turns out that at the time of writing, London's bus timetables are rather treated as a contract with the public. The public expect London's bus operators to meet the expectations of the timetable to some degree of accuracy to be counted as successful. What this means is that buses mostly arrive in less time than is expected. Or rather, bus operators set low expectations for the passengers. In this case, truth has been sacrificed and the timetable is used as a measure of success of the transport authorities. In many cases, this approach leads to passenger satisfaction, as passengers waiting for a bus are likely to often be pleasantly surprised by how early buses arrive. On the other hand, if they knew the truthful figures, it is possible that they could plan their journeys better.

A problem for authorities is that if there is no pre-set timetable, how can they measure their success? Achieving both truth and a measure of success would require two timetables – one to measure success against and one to provide the real data as to how well the buses are actually performing. By publishing the timetable that the authorities are measured against, the timetable becomes a contract that the authorities are happy to be held accountable to meet - in a way it is a truth, just not the truth of the actual arrival times. In London, bus operators are held accountable not exactly to a timetable. Transport for London uses a metric that measures the success of passenger journeys in general. This includes waiting times, crowding of a bus and the travel time of the bus. Bus operators are free to design the timetables themselves, but must conform to the standards set them, which are not published at the bus stops. This can come as a bit of a surprise, but the reasoning is that the metrics could be satisfied by different timetables. Authorities outsourcing bus operations to a third party have to give them some freedoms in which to operate and have to trust them with decisions to some extent.

When creating a timetable where buses should arrive every x minutes, some of the options that authorities have are:

1. A timetable used to measure the success of buses

   (a) Scoring bus operators on how close every subsequent bus arrival time is to x

   (b) Scoring bus operators on the amount of buses arriving in or less than the amount of time stated in the timetable

2. A timetable that is an empirical analysis of arrival times

   (a) Show live predicted arrival times

   (b) A statistical analysis of arrival times calculated over a significant period

   (c) A smart model that predicts how the day's timetable is likely to look based on a comparison of recent events with past data

Option 1a may be advantageous to passengers who like to plan their journeys accurately. However, this option results in increased travel times on that bus service. To ensure that buses can adhere to some arrival time x accurately, it would have to be a time that the vast majority of buses could meet. The buses that would have otherwise gone faster would have to wait at the bus stops to ensure they do not exceed this time. Therefore, buses will not be able to go faster than a bus that faces all the predicted obstacles on that route. Timetable efficiency would be sacrificed for its accuracy.

Option 1b is likely to result in a pessimistic timetable, where most buses arrive before the time they would be expected at. This is likely to happen, as bus operators would not be happy to sign a contract where they have to meet a time they cannot – therefore the expected arrival time will most likely be set at a higher time than is needed. The bus operator will then put in a lot of effort to meet the criteria, by increasing the frequency of buses on the route and by regulating the service. These two facts alone will mean that buses arrive more often than is stated in the timetable. The advantage of this situation is that passengers are rarely disappointed – buses will be arriving sooner than predicted, so passengers will get a feeling of luck that will accompany them for the rest of the journey, making it more pleasant. The bus operators would receive fewer complaints and would have a better public image. The disadvantage is that this option delves the furthest away from having a 'true' timetable. Neither the buses are trying to meet the timetable accurately, nor are the timetables a true measure of how often the buses arrive. When asked, the vast majority of people I talked to claimed they would prefer to know the real arrival times than be fed an inflated timetable – and yet it is obvious that option 1b naturally results in happier customers. The fact is, the customers are happier so long as they think that the timetable is true, while it is not. If that is the case, are the public happier only because they are being cheated? In a sense, that isn't necessarily true. The timetable is still a source of truth – it is what the buses are being run against, except they are called to outperform it. However, if the authorities were to avoid misleading the public, they should state on the timetables that the timetable is a contract that the buses run against, rather than a source of truth.

Option 2a (showing live arrival times) is a strategy that has been adopted by many transport authorities. It is usually added to support timetables rather than to replace them. Passengers waiting at bus stops can be shown an electronic display that will tell them how many minutes are left till the bus arrives. This can be helpful for people to decide whether they want to wait for a bus or whether they want to walk, or it can help plan a journey or even relieve anxiety (or cause it, depending on how late the bus is). However, there are some caveats. The method used to calculate the amount of time the bus should arrive in may be wrong. For example, a bus that is waiting at a set of traffic lights for 3 minutes, may have been displayed on a screen as *arriving in 8 minutes* for the whole duration of that time, meaning that it was certainly not true for at least two of those minutes. The situation gets even more complex as routes are filled with more and more obstacles that the bus has to pass. Getting greater accuracy is however difficult – situations on the road can change every minute or even every few seconds and this will ultimately have to be reflected in a live arrivals bus timetable.

2b (A statistical analysis of arrival times calculated over a significant period) is an option that would allow commuters to get a good understanding of the probabilities of a bus arriving in some amount of time. Recent analyses of distributions of bus arrival times could be displayed for people waiting at bus stops, displaying recent and relevant information as to how the buses are performing. This would also allow customers to get a better understanding of how well their bus operators perform, rather than linking such an opinion to their own anecdotal experience. Prospective passengers that know how reliable a bus route is can better plan their journey and risks associated with it. If people change bus routes because of low reliability or long wait times, the operators would have short term incentives to improve the bus route reliability that would be set by real customer preferences, as opposed to broader metrics set by local authorities who may not understand the motivations of passengers on particular routes.

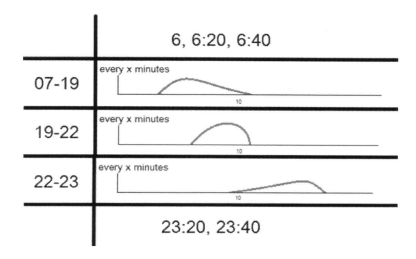

Figure 3.2: A vague idea of how a *true* empirical timetable could display an analysis of bus arrival times based on data from a significant period in the past.

It would be interesting to find out whether the average commuter would be interested in detailed timetables that show the probability of buses arriving at various times. If they would not, it should still be considered if the amount of people interested in it is sizeable. For timetables where detail is deemed unnecessary, the expected arrival times should be displayed in such a way that the minimum and maximum times include 2 standard deviations (95%) of the bus arrival times. If the expected arrival time band is then very wide, it will be obvious that the timetable is almost meaningless.

2c (A smart model that predicts how the day's timetable is likely to look based on a comparison of recent events with past data) is an option that combines the benefits of 2a and 2b. Electronic boards or websites accessible by smart devices could be used to display the distribution of probabilities of the next set of bus arrival times and of the bus timetable as it is likely to be affected by current disruptions on the day. A machine learning model would be trained to display the day's arrival times based on recent arrival times. This would be like option 2b, only the timetables would be better fit to the situation of the road and the buses on that route on that particular day. Providing such timetable data through an API could also allow mapping companies to better plan and predict journeys made on online mapping tools.

3.2.1   Live Bus Arrival Time Accountability

Now that live bus arrival times are displayed on screens at bus stops and on websites, this service has become an interface with the public. Commuters can be just as, or even more upset by incorrect live bus arrival times as with delayed buses. Live arrival times are supposed to be a more accurate and more trustworthy means of telling how long a person may have to wait for bus arrival times. This raises the question of whether the providers of the live bus arrival times should also be measured to see how well they perform. If a bus is stuck at *8 minutes away* for multiple minutes, this will be frustrating for customers and will be untrue of the data providers. It may be true in the sense that it **should** take 8 minutes for the bus to arrive within 8 minutes, but if it hasn't arrived within those 8 minutes, it can't really be said that it was 8 minutes away to begin with, as time has proven it false. To provide a better service to customers, it might be worth considering either providing a time band in which the bus would arrive within (using data to figure out the timespan which covers 95% of the times it has taken a bus to arrive at the bus stop from its current location). Predictions made at some arbitrary time could also be displayed somewhere and compared to real waiting times, to display how well a display has been predicting arrival times on that day. Authorities should take an interest in making the live arrival times as accurate, or at least as far from misinformation as possible. Hopefully with further improvements to live arrival times, public trust of transport authorities could increase even further.

If there is some display that shows how well the live arrival times are doing, how would the public know whether the arrival time checking system is trustworthy? Surely it is a public interface, so it should be checked? Such checks could go further and further down the rabbit hole where every system needs to be checked by a subsequent system. One way to avoid a need for infinite systems would be to open source the checking system and to let the public get involved in how arrival time success is measured. One could ask why we shouldn't just cut to the chase and open source the code that calculates the arrival times. That is certainly an option that could improve trust, but without a way of measuring how well it is performing, it cannot improve by much. If all bus data (real historical arrival and journey times) were published, this could be another way to ensure the public can check the quality of time arrival estimation services without a need for authorities to manage additional systems and displays. Any interested persons can already collect data as to what times are predicted via arrival time APIs, or could compare data displayed at actual bus stops to the real arrival times as published later.

3.3   How Long Should You Wait for a Bus?

Different people have different priorities when it comes to commuting. When using public transport, people can be led by a vast array of different strategies. Some people may be trying to get from one point to another as fast as possible. Some people are interested in travelling in such a way that there will be the least risk to their arrival time – so they can be on time to an important meeting or interview. Others are interested in minimising the amount of effort required to get to their destination.

For most people, decreasing the amount of time to get to a destination is a must. Mapping tools as provided online by Google, Bing, or Citymapper have proved immensely popular, particularly due to the fact that they can show which routes are the fastest. Unless commuters know an area really well, they are unlikely to be able to figure out a way to optimise a route to be faster than that suggested by a mapping tool.

Minimising the risk that one might be late can be a complex business. In terms of short distance routes, it can be a case of picking walking over other means of transport, so that the commuter will not be affected by potential traffic issues or public transport failures. When travelling over longer distances, it can be wise to pick routes where there are options for changing route along the way, so if the service faults while travelling one could switch to a different means of transport.

Reducing the amount of effort and improving ease of transport can mean less walking and active transport and more waiting for buses and trains. It can mean a choice of route where the person has to change trains or buses the least and can stay on the same vehicle for the longest. Reasons for reducing effort can be many – from disability to pure laziness. Some people enjoy using public transport and want to make it even more pleasant for themselves. Others like a simpler route, as it may allow them to watch a film or read a book – I certainly do.

However, most people are not looking for a single trait for their journey. For example, commuters may want the simplest journey possible but they would still like to be punctual.

In 2008, Justine Gejeune Chen, Scott Duke Kominers and Robert Wyatt Sinnott published an article that considered the problem of how one should decide how long to wait for a bus at a bus stop before giving up and walking[7]. The scenario described was that of a lazy mathematician who is trying to be punctual, but would like to take a journey with minimal effort. The bus covers the distance directly, but buses arrive sporadically at the bus stops. The article proves mathematically that the optimal solution for the mathematician is to wait for a bus, unless the time taken to walk the distance is less than the time the bus would take to drive the distance added to the time in which the bus is likely to arrive. The authors point out that walking to the next bus stop will only increase the amount of effort required for the journey and is unlikely to change the arrival time at all. 2 further papers have been written since, expanding and supporting this result[8][9]. Taking this result seriously would mean that in most cases, lazy people should always wait for a bus. But in the real world, one should always also check whether the buses are operating that stop at the time of waiting. The last line of the original paper points this out when it mentions that the mathematician had been too distracted with the walk/wait problem to notice that "it was a holiday, whence no busses were running". Another thing that has not yet been considered in any of the three papers is the fact that on highly busy routes, it can often be the case that buses are overcrowded and therefore passengers are not allowed on. Unpopular bus stops that follow popular bus stops can be a nightmare – buses may be filled in the

---

[7]Walk versus Wait: The Lazy Mathematician Wins, Justin G. Chen, Scott D. Kominers, Robert W. Sinnott https://arxiv.org/abs/0801.0297v3

[8]A Note on Walking Versus Waiting, Anthony B. Morton https://arxiv.org/abs/0802.3653

[9]A Note on Walk versus Wait: Lazy Mathematician Wins, Ramnik Arora https://arxiv.org/abs/0803.3106

popular bus stop almost all day, meaning that a customer waiting on the following bus stop may not be able to board a bus for hours. In these cases, it can be worthwhile walking back a stop, to where it may be possible to get on before the other people. Alternatively, if there is a stop in the direction of the bus' travel where passengers are likely to alight, it might be worth walking forwards to that stop.

My personal experience with the London Underground suggests to me that there is a similar problem in situations where services become suspended. When the tube lines that I am taking home have suddenly become suspended, I have often found that taking an alternative, more complex route just isn't worth the effort. The service usually resumes normal service within an hour or less, but the fact I can wait in a train or on just one platform means I can easily read my book without the distraction of rearranging my journey. What could be particularly useful for commuters who think the way I do, might be some analysis regarding how quickly services on the Underground are restored, based on the kind of fault that the line is experiencing. If the data could be provided offline in a mobile app, users could conclude what their best options were based on information on a service outage gained from tube staff.

3.4   Reliability as a Result of Law

There is no escaping transport. Even if someone is housebound, they rely on transport for their food, post and any other essentials. This fact means that almost every branch of law has to also restrict transport in some way. Transport providers have to be aware of laws ranging from property law to health and safety and data protection. The law is intended to ensure the wellbeing of those it applies to, but the difficulties of crafting good laws are immense. A well-intended law that seems an obvious solution to a lot of problems can often have unforeseen circumstances that may cause greater problems in the long run. Other laws are made on arbitrary points of division between multiple options which cannot all be satisfied together. In this section, we will look at a few laws that shape transport operations and consider the difficulties faced by lawmakers.

3.4.1 How Flight Operators Can Delay Multiple Journeys to Avoid Fines

On 11th February 2004, the European Parliament took it upon itself to issue Regulation (EC) No 261/2004, establishing common rules on compensation and assistance to passengers in the event of cancelled or delayed flights[10]. This piece of legislation has a set of rules that standardise how flight operators should behave if their passengers' flights are delayed, including duty of care and any payment of fines[11].

Of particular interest to this section are Articles 6 and 7. Both of them are valid if the flight is delayed by:

1. Two hours on flights of 1500km or less

2. Three hours or more in the case of all intra-Community flights of more than 1500km and of all other flights between 1500 and 3500km

3. Four hours on any flights not falling under (a) or (b).

---

[10](EC) No 261/2004 https://eur-lex.europa.eu/LexUriServ/LexUriServ.do?uri=CELEX:32004R0261:en:HTML

[11]Some other rules can also affect flight operators. For example, Council Regulation (EEC) No. 95/93 presents a method of collaboration between operators and airports, where airports will allocate slots in the timetable for flights for operators. If the operator does not use their slot at least 80% of the time, they can lose this slot.

Article 6 states that in these cases, the flight operators have a duty of care and therefore, depending on the circumstances, may have to offer food, a bed and other necessities for the duration of the delay. Article 7 states that in these cases, the customers have a right to compensation of EUR 250, 400 and 600 in cases (a), (b) and (c) respectively. This compensation can be lowered by 50% if the flight operators can provide the customers with an alternative means of travel that will let them reach their destination in 2, 3 and 4 hours respectively.

This law provides a very clear financial incentive for flight operators to ensure that flights aren't delayed by the specified amounts. However, flight operators have methods of circumventing the issue that may not be wonderful for passengers on the wider scale.

Flight delays can occur for a number of reasons. But in this case we will only look at the case where the fault that causes the delay is in the flight operator's control. Airline faults can be attributed in cases of lack of crew or mechanical issues on planes that could have been prevented by routine maintenance. In these cases, passengers that would be catching a flight on that plane will now require a different plane. The best way for the passenger to guard for these kinds of scenarios is to have additional planes and pilots on hold that are otherwise not scheduled to fly on a day. However, planes and pilots on hold would mean that the flight operators are not running their business as efficiently as they could be doing otherwise – they could be delivering more passengers to destinations with this plane and making more money, after all! If all the planes are being used, then the passengers will have to wait till a moment where a plane has some time free in its schedule in order to be able to take the delayed passengers to their destination. The time to wait for a free slot in the flight schedule could be very long. It would certainly exceed the time limits set by the EU, so the flight operators would have the additional expenses of providing care and compensation to the customers.

The smart alternative for the flight operators in this scenario is to figure out a way to juggle around their available planes in order to ensure the time limits set in (EC) No 261/2004 are not exceeded. The switching of planes between flights is likely to result in delays for a wider amount of flights, albeit at a much lower delay time.

Therefore, the law becomes a mechanism where a single long delay transforms into multiple delays, which can potentially last a whole day – till night time, when there are no further flights, meaning there is bound to be an additional plane to cover the shifting of planes in the schedule. Is this the result the law was trying to achieve? Is it better for passengers of multiple flights to be delayed some amount in order to stop the passengers of a single flight being delayed a longer amount? Certainly a very long delay can ruin the plans of the people on that flight – but surely there are also people on tighter schedules whose plans may be ruined even with a shorter delay that may not allow for compensation?

If we assume that shorter delays are not particularly problematic for passengers, the planning of journeys involving flights become highly inefficient. Passengers taking flights of 1500km or less are unlikely to want to book a particular train at their destination, as they may want to be able to select the earliest train within a 2 hour compensation period following the flight, in order to make their journey the quickest. But picking an early train may mean that they will miss it, and the flight operators will not refund its cost. The only viable option for pre-booking trains will be the case where they book a train just under 2 hours after arrival, meaning that if they miss it, they will be refunded. Such an option means that the journey is by default taking 2 hours more now, due to the padding they require for the after-flight train. Most flights in Europe are under 1500km, and a lot of them take under 2 hours. This now means that the journey time is doubled if the passenger wants to book a train upon arrival without a risk of refund if the flight is delayed. Is it truly worse if one flight was delayed by 3 hours, than if hundreds of flights were delayed by 1 hour? What are the possible alternatives?

One way could be to have a flat profile of penalty charges leading up to the times specified by the law. So flights under 1500km would be refunded to the passengers by the amount they were delayed by, divided by 2 hours, topping out at the full refund rate once the full 2 hours are met. A 1000km flight that was 1 hour late would have the passengers receive half the flight's cost back. These charges would have to be limited to cases where the flight operators would be found to be at fault. Such a law would mean that flight operators would want to minimise the total number of hours of delays on their flights. Making passengers on multiple flights suffer because of issues with one flight would then most likely not be a viable option.

However, there are also problems for the passengers with such a penalty charge scheme. One advantage of the current law is the very fact that flight operators don't have to pay any fines in the majority cases. By juggling the various planes and scheduled flights, the operators can avoid paying a fine. This means that they can keep their fares low. The moment that flights start incurring more fines, the operators would have to factor in this additional risk and cost into the cost of their flights. Cheap flights would become unsustainable for most flight operators and fares would increase. Rail and Bus companies can pad their timetables, but there are established flight times for planes which the flight operators would find hard to avoid.

3.4.2 Deregulated Buses

When a particular bus service is performing poorly, one would think that it would surely be best if it were possible for there to be some bus operator that could come and save the day by putting many buses on this route. Bus operators could use freely available data to see which routes are performing poorly and jump onto those routes in order to gain from the fact that it is likely that there will be many people who will want to take a bus on that route.

The deregulation of buses in 1986 may have allowed a large amount of innovation, but it was devastating for rural areas[12]. Bus operators who may have been operating rural areas would immediately realise that moving their services to more urban areas would be far more profitable. As a consequence, few bus operators remained in rural areas. Another problem that came with the deregulation was the lack of stability in the network. Operators could send a 42-day notice to re-register timetables and therefore change them in as much time[13]. Timetables were constantly changing, which was confusing for commuters. In some cases, operators were even battling out on routes and re-registering bus routes in short succession to try to counter the re-registrations of competing companies.

The issues raised by the deregulation resulted in measures that tried to reduce the negative effects of the bus arms race. The Greater Lon-

---

[12]Paul Fawcett Managing Passenger Logistics: The Comprehensive Guide to People and Transport 2000 p.32

[13]Paul Fawcett Managing Passenger Logistics: The Comprehensive Guide to People and Transport 2000 p.34

don Authority Act 1999 allowed Transport for London to regulate the bus services in London, while the Local Transport Act 2008 gave powers to Passenger Transport Executives to be the sole transport planning authorities in their areas[14].

---

[14]At the time of writing there are 6 PTEs – Transport for Greater Manchester, Merseyside Passenger Transport Executive, South Yorkshire Passenger Transport Executive, Tyne and Wear Passenger Transport Executive, Transport for West Midlands and West Yorkshire Passenger Transport Executives.

4.   *Mysterious Traffic Jams*

Sometimes when driving down a motorway there will occasionally be a traffic jam that in a short while resolves itself without ever showing an actual reason as to why the cars were slowing down and sometimes even stopping. This chapter will dive into the study of traffic behaviour and will show how the behaviour of individual vehicles can have a large effect on the rest of the network.

4.1   Reductionist Car Traffic Modelling

While many of the topics in science can be analysed and understood at the level they are studied at, sometimes it is necessary to reduce a problem to its components to understand a situation. To get a good understanding of our mysterious motorway traffic jams, it would be good to understand how vehicles behave at the unit level. We will now study what factors affect a vehicle's movement and how it relates to other vehicles around it.

One of the first things to consider with automobiles is that they do not use the same signalling mechanisms that are present in rail transport. Modern cars may have autonomous emergency braking (AEB), which provides a lot more safety, but most vehicles are still dependant on the driver's reaction time[1]. The reaction time, along with the degree of aggressiveness and familiarity of the area being driven in are the biggest factors that affect a single vehicle on a road[2].

The environment surrounding a vehicle has a big effect on how it will behave. This should be obvious, in that a bend in the road will result in a vehicle turning, but there are many more details that will affect how the driver drives. This can be due to the urbanisation of the area, the width of the road, the slope of the road, any signals and signs that are present on the road, and weather conditions.

As soon as further vehicles are added to the road, an additional area of study becomes important – the interaction between the vehicles. One of the more important things for modellers is to understand how a vehicle behaves in relation to the vehicle in front of it. These models are called *car-following* models, even though the vehicles may only be following each other temporarily[3]. An early model called the PITT model

---

[1] The American Association of State Highway and Transportation Officials (2011) gives the following formula for Stopping Sight Distance: $SSD = 1.47vt + 1.075\frac{v^2}{a}$ where v is the velocity, t the reaction time and a is the deceleration rate. The first term in this equation is the distance travelled during the time it takes the driver to react, while the second term is the actual time taken to stop with the brakes applied. The two constants 1.47 and 1.075 are a result of the AASHTO using the ridiculous units of ft/s^2 for a and mph for v, resulting in a need for unit conversion. One thing that the equation makes quite clear is that the effect of reduced reaction time (e.g. when drunk driving) has a huge effect on the SSD – the additional time taken to react will be multiplied directly by the velocity.

[2] Lily Elefteriadou, An Introduction to Traffic Flow Theory (2014) Springer p.22

[3] Pedestrian traffic can also be modelled with leader-follower models, but as soon as there is a loss of a structured lane of traffic these models become anisotropic models – ones where they are affected by anything in front of them. The distinction is that anisotropic models do not assume that other vehicles or pedestrians in front of the one being studied are going to be travelling in the same direction. Further information on anisotropic walker

(named after the fact it was developed at the University of Pittsburgh) assumes that a following vehicle will attempt to keep the same safe headway between it and the car in front[4]. If the vehicle in front slows down, the following vehicle will also slow down, in order to maintain that safe headway. The interesting thing about this model is that it ignores any non-kinematic factors, such as reaction times, which we know exist from our consideration of single vehicles. The model has a few parameters that can be fitted to real data, and after fitting, it will give a rough estimate as to how vehicles will behave on a road.

4.2 A Wave of Traffic

The Gipps Model is a car-following model that takes into account a reaction time, as well as a concept of *constrained speed* – where the following vehicle cannot reach the speed it desires because of the lead vehicle.

The Gipps model is a much better predictor of car-following scenarios than the PITT model. It often predicts periods of short and long spaces between vehicles earlier or later than is present in reality[5], but it also predicts behaviours that are very similar to what is seen on real roads. This makes it a much better model for building simulations. One should remember that a small difference at any point on a trip can make

models can be found in Hoogendoorn and Daamen's *A Novel Calibration Approach of Microscopic Pedestrian Models in Timmerman's Pedestrian Behavior: Models, Data Collection and Applications* p.197.

[4]And for those interested, the PITT model is wonderfully explained in Lily Elefteriadou's An Introduction to Traffic Flow Theory (2014) Springer p.39. I considered putting the equation for the car following model in, but it barely fitted onto two lines, which suggested to me that it may not provide the simplicity in understanding a reader may expect from an equation.

[5]Lily Efteriadou An Introduction to Traffic Flow Theory (2014) Springer, p. 48.

a big difference in how traffic predictions behave, so a perfect prediction is almost impossible. Improving the similarity between model and reality is a job that will most likely never cease requiring further work.

As soon as the PITT model is replaced by the Gipps model, models begin to witness a phenomenon known as "traffic oscillations". Vehicles do not neatly increment or decrement their speed. If a lead vehicle slows down, a following vehicle may slow down more than it needs to[6], and then speed up again to match the new speed of the lead vehicle. If you repeat this many times down a road, the vehicles much further down the road may witness much greater differences between top speed and lowest speed. This effect is greater in size if the vehicles on the road were closer together before the lead vehicle changed speed[7]. If vehicles are far enough apart, their braking is usually smoother and smaller in size. The following vehicle may in fact not slow down as much as the lead vehicle did initially, meaning that large distances between vehicles can even cancel out the effect of traffic oscillations.

While the traffic oscillations happen clearly in models and simulations, how prevalent are they in reality? Experiments with real vehicles have shown this to occur with real vehicles[8] and there is plenty of footage

---

[6]In fact, it may need to slow down more to deal with the fact that the driver's reaction time will result in the following vehicle coming closer to the lead vehicle than it should be, requiring a slowing down to reset the safe distance between them.

[7]The differences in effect size based on distance between vehicles can be seen particularly well in this simulation https://traffic-simulation.de/ring.html – if you block the road at a point and then remove the blocking object straight away afterwards, the traffic jam in the lane nearest the centre (where vehicles are closer together) will have a much larger effect size than the outer lane.

[8]As seen particularly well in this video: https://www.youtube.com/watch?v=P7xx9uH2i7w&app=desktop

showing that it occurs on real roads[9].

If vehicles are close together, the traffic oscillations can result in vehicles that are far behind the lead vehicle coming to a stop. The lead vehicle doesn't necessarily have to slow down by much either – the combination of reactions of drivers down a road can aggregate from a small amount of braking into a choc-a-block traffic jam. Interestingly, this traffic jam also moves like a Mexican wave backwards down the road, meaning that if you experience such a traffic jam, it will most likely not be occurring anywhere near where the initial driver applied the brakes.

So our conundrum of strange traffic jams seems to have been demystified. But what can be done about this phenomenon? Obviously it is clear now that keeping a greater distance between vehicles can help. Traffic authorities can also develop smarter motorways to deal with these scenarios. If there is a traffic jam up ahead, variable speed limits can slow down the vehicles coming up to the jam before the drivers could see it. If the vehicles far behind are slowed down enough, the vehicles in the jam could leave it before the vehicles behind start joining it. Then the traffic jam will be resolved.

4.3 The Relationship Between Flow and Speed

The relationships between traffic variables can be far more complex than is initially assumed. For example, it would be clear to most people that if vehicles travel at higher speeds, it will increase the traffic flow. This is clearly the case in a simplistic imaginary scenario, but it isn't true for all cases of roads. On real roads, the relationship between speed and traffic flow is subject to the relationship of both variables, along with the

---

[9]As particularly well illustrated by this gif: https://imgur.com/fLNs3k0

amount of vehicles present on the road. While roads are fairly empty vehicles will usually start by travelling at a constant speed (the speed limit on that road). In this initial scenario, traffic flow will increase proportionally with the amount of vehicles that are added. Eventually there will be so many vehicles on the road that bottlenecks in the road will start to form and the speed of the vehicles will slow down. Traffic flow may still increase as the speed decreases, but eventually both speed and traffic flow will decrease as vehicles flood the route.

The interesting thing to see is that there can be multiple speeds at which we have the same traffic flow. It is possible to achieve the same traffic flow in a slow moving traffic jam by stopping all the vehicles and sending them out one by one at much higher speeds. However, ensuring that the traffic is still moving, even if the pace is slow can have psychological benefits for drivers, who will at least feel they are constantly progressing, rather than starting and stopping.

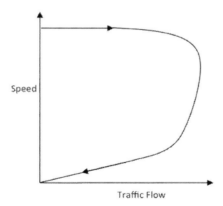

Figure 4.1: As the amount of cars on a route increase, both speed and traffic flow can decrease.

The interesting thing to see is that there can be multiple speeds at which we have the same traffic flow. It is possible to achieve the same traffic flow in a slow moving traffic jam by stopping all the vehicles and sending them out one by one at much higher speeds. However, ensuring that the traffic is still moving, even if the pace is slow can have psychological benefits for drivers, who will at least feel they are constantly progressing, rather than starting and stopping.

This relationship, where speed and traffic flow eventually become tiny with increased usage explains well how in 2002 London's traffic was so bad that the average speed was the same as that of horse-drawn carts in the nineteenth century, with vehicles typically spending half of their journey time in queues[10].

Another thing that is interesting to think about, is that if a road has vehicles travelling with close-to peak traffic flow, it can make little difference whether they are slowing down for a bit, and then going faster – as they slow down, they will bunch, increasing density, and as they speed up, density increases and speed increases. This way of thinking about traffic can help one understand that traffic oscillations do not necessarily mean that there is an overall reduction in traffic flow.

4.4 Improving the Driving Experience

4.4.1 Replace or Augment?

As new technologies have emerged, the driver's interface with the vehicle has changed considerably. Manual gear sticks have been replaced with automatic gearboxes that require minimum input. Power steering has reduced the amount of effort needed to turn the vehicle. Controls are both

---

[10]David Williams and Tim Parr Enterprise Programme Management – Delivery Value, Deloitte, 2004 p.150

becoming simpler and allowing more options. Electronic screens are replacing mechanical levers, switches and wheels. More and more parts of vehicles are slowly being taken control of by the machines. Is it correct for us to cede power to the machines, or should we be empowering our own skills and abilities?

Some of the steps recently taken in automotive technology have given unprecedented control to computers. Autonomous Emergency Braking (AEB) (that is now mandatory in all new heavy vehicles since 2015) applies brakes immediately when it senses that a vehicle is at risk of collision. Lane centring (or auto steer) technologies help keep vehicles within their lanes on motorways, taking away the task of steering from the driver. Neither technology is supposed to be a system the owner relies on – rather a backup that gets into gear if the driver is not reacting properly. Drivers using such systems are still expected to keep their hands on the wheel and brake appropriately. The unusual aspect of these technologies is that they override the driver, taking control of the vehicle. While these can be life-saving in cases where a driver is falling asleep, or is already distracted, they can also lead to dangerous scenarios. With AEB, if a vehicle makes a mistake and brakes in a situation where it should not have it can lead to a crash if the vehicle behind was not a sufficient distance away. Both AEB and lane centering technologies can lead to behavioural adaptations that can even make drivers stop concentrating on the road[11]. Can drivers be expected to remain as alert when many of

---

[11]While *Lommatzsch v. Tesla Inc et al* may lead to a view that Tesla was in fact responsible for misleading drivers to think that their vehicle was fully autonomous (plausibly also for some of the similar cases such as *Handan China Jan 20 2016* [crash with a stationary truck], *Williston Florida May 7 2016* [crash with a turning tractor-trailer], *Culver City California Jan 22 2018* [where the driver was drinking a coffee and eating a bagel] and *Moscow Russia Aug 10 2019* [where the driver claimed his hands were on the wheel, but that he was not

their decisions are becoming less relevant[12]? Surely we could be using all of the information that could be gathered and feeding it to the driver, augmenting their abilities rather than discarding them?

Cruise, or speed control is a fairly old technology, having been developed to some measure in steam engines. In modern cars, it is usually controlled and turned on or off easily from the control panel, setting a speed limit for normal use of the gas pedal, but allowing the driver to override it by pressing the pedal fully down[13]. It has been suggested recently that vehicles should be fitted with cruise control that could take a feed from GPS signals and allow the local speed limit to be applied as the maximum speed. Is this case a replacement or an augmentation of the driver's skills? I would argue that it depends on how the interface between driver and vehicle is designed. If the driver is warned as the speed limit changes - allowing the driver to change the cruise control setting – then I would call that an augmentation. If the new speed limit is applied without an input from the driver, then that is a replacement of

---

paying attention]), it is certainly still the case that previous driving experiences with the vehicles made drivers trust the technology to keep them safe.

[12]Software developers may be aware of the concept of the *Irony of Automation* – which refers to the fact that as a system becomes more reliable, human operators do less and they therefore pay less attention to the system. All in all, this means that more reliable systems are harder to monitor for errors. So while this may be a fairly new topic in the field of self-driving vehicles, the concepts are not particularly new. One way of dealing with this problem for drivers is a method already employed in Japanese and Chinese rail – pointing and calling. Your style of pointing and calling can also improve to increase this effect (robotic/military pointing and calling can in fact increase errors, so there is a knack to it!). A study worth reading is Shigemori, Sato, Masuda & Haga's Human error prevention effect of point and call check used by railway workers in Japan from Dadashi, Scott, Wilson and Mills' Rail Human Factors: Supporting reliability, safety and cost reduction (2013) CRC Press, Taylor & Francis Group p.605

[13]Or using a similar mechanism – this will depend on the vehicle model.

control. Personally, I support the former approach. I once accidentally turned the cruise control on in my car while on a motorway. The car was suddenly slowing down and I was distracted as I fumbled to turn it off. It is difficult to explain how much of a distraction it was if one hasn't experienced it. The sudden physical feeling of loss of control of acceleration in itself confuses the brain. Fortunately I wasn't in a complex driving situation, but GPS feeds could include many mistakes that would result in more dangerous situations – at road crossings and when the GPS technology will have the inevitable failures that will result in miscalculations of location. If accidents occur partially caused by these failures, who will take the blame – the driver, the car manufacturers or the GPS providers? The advantage of using the technology as an augmentation is that drivers will still be able to hold responsibility of their actions and will be able to act upon new information without relying on assumptions made by scientists and engineers who may not have predicted the particular scenarios in which the drivers may find themselves.

Part of the problem with augmentations is the side effects they can have on drivers. While additional information seems like it is something you would always want to have, the action of providing it –and what that will result in – can lead to difficulties. Collision avoidance technologies[14] are becoming a common feature in modern cars, even though it is still not fully established whether they help the driver focus on the safety-critical information or whether they delay drivers from taking evasive action due to the distraction they cause[15]. What can we

---

[14]Such as Forward Collision Warning (FCW) systems (which alert the driver when their vehicle is at risk of collision), or indeed AEB.

[15]Kristie L. Young and Michael A. Regan *Relationship between Behavioural Adaptation and Driver Distraction* from Christina M. Rudin-Brown and Samantha L. Jamson's *Behavioural Adaptation and Road Safety* p.232

make of all of this then? Are driving assistance technologies all bad and likely to cause issues? Certainly more studies need to be conducted, but maybe both driving skills and augmentation technologies may have to develop by quite an amount to ensure a safer road environment. We certainly should continue exploring what technologies can keep us safer, but in the context of how our behaviour will also respond to the new technologies we are to consume[16].

4.5 Bonini's Paradox

As we learn more and more about traffic problems and construct better and better models that represent reality better, we start delving into the realm of Bonini's paradox. This paradox states that as a model becomes more complex, it is less understandable – and therefore potentially less useful. An easy way to understand this problem is to think about maps. Maps are usually drawn much smaller than the area they represent, using symbols that group and simplify the functions of buildings, roads and land features. If a bit more detail is needed to see more local paths, or to better differentiate between two buildings, the map needs to be much bigger to cover the same amount of space. If we continued this progression to the point where the map is the size of the area it represents (think a map of England that is the size of England when lain out), it is not only useless because it is too big to hold and move – it is also useless because it does not simplify planning a journey to actually going on the journey without the map, or it is useless because it would be easier to look around to see what is around you than to look at the map

---

[16]For some ideas of how this could be done, Mark S. Young and Oliver Carsten's *Designing for Behavioural Adaptation* from Christina M. Rudin-Brown and Samantha L. Jamson's *Behavioural Adaptation and Road Safety* is a good starting point.

itself[17].

How useful a model is and how understandable it is are not quite the same, though[18]. While the 20th century saw a wonderful development of statistical models and detailed understanding of specific scenarios in the sciences, the start of the 21st century has seen a change in the approach to studying complex systems. This has been a result in the high growth of computing power, which has allowed us to leverage computational techniques to build complex statistical models.

Machine learning techniques ranging from multiple linear regression to deep neural networks allow us to build complex models based on many variables that can predict outcomes very well. The models built

---

[17]Any young people reading this who may not have any experience using a paper map may find it easier to imagine a mapping app that is so detailed that it only shows you which way to travel in millimetre increments – you would have to keep your eyes glued to the app at all times while travelling, rather than being able to glance and be aware of the turns you may need to take in the near future.

[18]Although being able to understand the model can be useful both for building better models that incorporate more detail and for what can be done with them. For example, models of pedestrians often use 3 variables - capacity of a link, maximum flow and the zero density (density of people at which their velocity approaches zero due to overcrowding). Various models have predicted these variables to be between $1.2 - 1.8(ms)^-1$, $1.75 - 7m^-2$ and $3.8 - 10m^-1$ respectively [Andreas Schadschneider and Armin Seyfried *Empirical results for Pedestrian Dynamics and their Implications for Cellular Automata Models (2009)* from Harry Timmermans' *Pedestrian Behavior: Models, Data Collection and Applications (2009)* Emerald Group Publishing p.30]. This is a huge variation which could be due to a number of factors, such as: cultural and population differences; differences between uni- and multi-directional flow; short-ranged fluctuations; and psychological factors given by the incentive of the movement or type of traffic. In this case, a better understanding of the minutiae of the models can help authorities improve policies and design of public spaces to help the public better. This does not however necessarily mean the model needs to be an expert system – investigating detail of a model could also be done by splitting machine learning models into parts.

using these techniques are referred to as "black boxes" in computer science. This is because we can only know what is going into and coming out of the boxes - we cannot fully understand how the internal parts of the system actually work[19]. While we cannot fully understand these models, they have a lot of potential. By training them on live data, we can make them predict outcomes to pretty high degrees of accuracy[20]. However, the problems with such models occur precisely around the edges where we do not understand them.

A self-driving car I tried out kept seeing *ghost vehicles* and swerving to avoid them. Healthcare algorithms can end up becoming racially biased[21]. Even my wife showed me an example where automated media target marketing was resulting in her seeing depressing stories of miscarriage and infant death during her pregnancy. None of these results were intended, and once the model designers are aware of it, they can try to

---

[19]To be more specific, we know why these techniques and algorithms work, but a specific model that is built can reach its stage in multiple ways, and we can never fully understand exactly what decisions this model will make, what scenarios may make it fail and how we can improve it without just rewriting the whole model.

[20]Or other measure, depending on what sort of data and model you are working with. For example, in classification models (for example, where you try to say whether an input is a bird, a plane or superman), you would probably be looking at a balance between Precision and Recall. Precision is the amount of true positives, over the amount of total positives – or the ratio between things you identified correctly against the total things you tried to identify. Recall is the amount of true positives divided by the total actual positives – or the ratio between things you identified correctly against all the things you should have identified correctly. If you want more precision, you will usually have to sacrifice some recall, and vice versa. Depending on your scenario, you may want more of one over the other. For example, if you were using facial recognition to help you tag images in social media, you might want to have a higher recall, so that users are more likely to be given the correct suggestions for tagging the pictures. If you were charging vehicle owners on a road, you may want a higher precision to stop you falsely charging users who were never there.

[21]Obermeyer, Z., Powers, B., Vogeli, C. & Mullainathan, S. Science 336, 447–453 (2019).

build new models that take the new scenarios into account. However, there will always be additional boundaries that the designers would not have thought about. There will always be scenarios where these models will fail, and if we do not understand the models we cannot predict them.

If we build expert systems[22], we will also eventually reach models that are too complex to understand. This is all too familiar a scenario – as we have learnt more, it has become harder and harder to claim to know the full extent of even a sub-domain of a scientific field. Software engineers working on enterprise systems will often accept that they cannot understand their full system and will aim to at least have a strong enough collective expertise on it to ensure they can continue work on it. Models built by human hand are prone to errors, but they also have some advantages. If someone wants to understand how a particular scenario is dealt with, they can gather the knowledge necessary for it from those involved in building it and tweak the system to fix it[23]. Models built through machine learning will only allow knowledge of the result of a scenario if you are able to recreate that scenario exactly, and will require a rebuilding of the model with new data to be able to handle the scenario. Is this that much of a difference? The machine learning model will be the far simpler and more obvious option in cases where you can easily acquire or generate the data necessary to train it. Systems

---

[22]Expert systems are ones that are designed by hand and using the knowledge of experts in the domain.

[23]For the really pedantic software developers reading this, they may point out that tweaking an enterprise system may have unforeseen side-effects and so isn't as simple as seen. Luckily such systems are (usually) built with extensive testing, so anything that could break functionality that has been deemed important enough to test will be found out and fixed at short notice.

that are safety-critical can be built with a different approach. In cases where sufficient requirements can be gathered, systems can be designed using formal methods. These are mathematical methods that can ensure that all plausible states of the system are proven to work as designed. Engineers working on some medical or aviation technologies would not consider any less reliability a real option for developing their systems.

Whatever technique is used for the development of models, eventually Bonini's paradox will kick in. The eventual result is one where the model becomes similarly complex to the reality it represents. It becomes harder and harder to make progress with developing the model, as being capable of doing it requires a thorough understanding of both reality and the model itself. Both goal will by this point be unachievable and differences will become harder and harder to find. This is precisely why scientific fields have become more and more specialised, and this is also why the future will require more and more specialisation in building and developing transport models – both academic and corporate.

5. *Expand the Infrastructure?*

CITIES develop and expand, growing every day. Upwards into the skies with tower blocks and outwards with the constant creation of suburbs until they start engulfing surrounding towns or even merge with other cities. This is usually not solely due to the growth of the population in the city itself, but also often due to migration - both from the countryside and often from other countries. Success is a magnet that attracts others hoping to see some of it for themselves.

Unfortunately, building new housing space isn't really sufficient to provide everything necessary to live a life. New schools, hospitals, emergency service stations, and entertainment facilities are rarely added at an appropriate rate, meaning many things in life can become more difficult. To continue this discussion much further would be out of scope of this book, but we can at least discuss the problems of expanding transport infrastructure.

5.1 Costs

In order to avoid an elephant entering the room, let us mention costs straight away. If there is indeed a housing crisis and people need housing, then the housing is the central part of the solution to the problem. Attaching this with the many more costs of new rail services and bus networks is going to add costs that won't necessarily be solving the primary problem. Cost cutting is always going to be a big part of any budget, and every item on a budget will be weighed against other items on a priority list. Transport is not often at the top of the list, as it is easy to think that if the housing is attached to a road network, it will be possible to solve the transport problems further down the line. Governments also have powers to buy up land and demolish buildings if they want to lay new railway lines, so planning ahead for rail isn't a prerequisite either.

There is of course the fact that many areas grow due to having existing transport options. One of the best examples of this would be Las Vegas, which started as a small station on a railway line, and has grown into a huge city. But it is still easy to find its original centre by the fact that it has a grid structure that is aligned with the railway line, while the urban planners later decided to adopt a grid system aligned with the compass points.

However, the problem of not planning for transport up front often means that expanding the transport infrastructure in this area later down the line becomes more expensive. Governments that want to install rail lines can certainly buy up land, but they have to do it at a premium, and often with legal cases brought against them that they need to quash with expert legal teams. Adding new bus routes may mean digging up and replacing sections of road to make space for bus stops and expanding

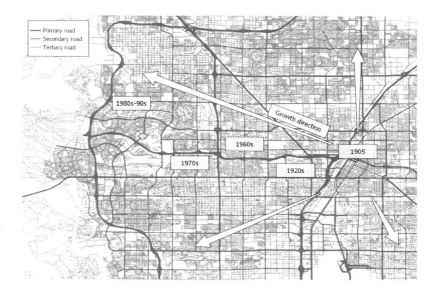

Figure 5.1: The change in urban design by decade can be clearly seen from above in the grid system of the roads in Las Vegas. Street Data from OpenStreetMap, available under the Open Database License.

pedestrian areas. On the bigger scale, introducing new landing strips and airports becomes almost impossible in developed cities, where citizens will create significant opposition to the noise and additional traffic despite the fact that it may bring an economic boost to the region.

Investment in infrastructure can also cause gentrification - that is, the displacement of the poor. Housing with poor transport infrastructure is often cheaper, as it is considered to be in a less attractive location due to fewer connections. If money is invested to improve the infrastructure, the house prices can go up and bring in wealthier people. This can draw in businesses that target wealthier people often by having higher prices and soon enough original citizens of the area can be priced out and forced to leave.

Transport planners are unlikely to worry about gentrification, since they are pretty one-minded as to what problems they are solving. They are ultimately most interested in efficiency and safety. But it's worth noting that changes that seem to be an obvious improvement may have side-effects down the line that cause challenges for people whose situations were not considered.

5.1.1 Safety

With many forms of transport, it becomes more and more expensive to increase the efficiency of the mode of transport slightly as the efficiency increases. In the meantime, safety can usually be increased linearly with investment. The combination of these two facts means that modes that already have large investments in them can have a big effect on safety with further investment, or a small effect on efficiency[1]. Investors are more likely to want to see their money making larger improvements, so it makes more sense to put further investments into improving safety rather than efficiency[2].

When making decisions as to how to fund a safety improvement, options can be beneficial for different reasons. For example, an investor is

---

[1] *Systematic and Customer Driven Approach to Cost-Efficiently Improving Interlocking and Signaling in Train Transport* Jorn Schlingensiepen, Florin Nemtanu Referenced from *Rail Transport – Systems Approach (Studies in Systems, Decision and Control volume 87)* p.250.

[2] It is especially worthwhile investing in making sure people feel safe on public transport. A rail accident can result in a huge loss of journeys and therefore a loss in ticket sales for months or even years afterwards, even though the risk of travelling on that mode of transport will be no riskier. Absolute safety is impossible and most events (such as the King's Cross fire on the London Underground in 1987) happen without any possibility of prediction and therefore prevention. Therefore, anyone investing in transport needs to both ensure it is safe and that people realise the risks are low and feel comfortable going on it. See John Glover's *Principles of Railway Operation* (2013) Ian Allan Publishing p.17 for a further discussion on the subject.

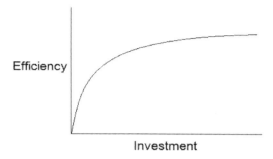

Figure 5.2: As more and more investment is put into transport efficiency, the return on investment starts to diminish.

likely to be faced with one option that has the maximum net savings and one option that maximizes benefit in relation to the cost. For example, an option A can save £700,000 at a cost of £200,000, while option B can save £900,000 at a cost of £300,000. Option A will be the most cost effective (with a benefit/cost ratio of 3.5 vs 3), while option B will have the biggest net savings (£100,000 more) [3][4]. The additional savings can be seen to hold more importance when one considers that this has made people actually safer. However, the lack of cost efficiency also suggests that the money may have been better spent on other programmes that could be invested in safety elsewhere.

---

[3]Example taken from Gerald J. S. Wilde's *Applying the Risk-Homeostatic Dynamics to Improvement of Safety* from Rudin-Brown and Jamson's *Behavioural Adaptation and Road Safety* p.395.

[4]It is worth noting that some safety programmes can have far higher returns on value. For example, a programme involving financial incentives in the US had a benefit/cost ratio of 19 to 1, saving over $2.4 billion on the company's workers compensation bill. Incentive programmes can lead people to under-report accidents, but mostly in minor accidents only (see Gerald J. S. Wilde's *Applying the Risk-Homeostatic Dynamics to Improvement of Safety* from Rudin-Brown and Jamson's *Behavioural Adaptation and Road Safety* p.390).

5.2 Non-Functional Problems

Many of the problems involved in improving transport networks are quite unexpected and are almost impossible to predict. There are no experts one can hire that would cover the huge range of problems that can occur from any single change. This is even more so, as a single change to a transport network can also have side-effects stemming from the initial effect and therefore can only realistically be reacted to, rather than planned.

5.2.1 Diverse Opinions

People are diverse and so are their opinions. Therefore, when a transport authority decides on a strategy, it may make many people happy while also upsetting others. This can be in cases where an advantage to some commuters brings about a disadvantage to other commuters. It can also occur in cases where some people love a particular change, while others are indifferent to it[5] and may therefore be unhappy that their payments or taxes are going towards such pointless improvements. People will often have their own ideas for which problems transport authorities should be solving and how they should solve them. These will often be in conflict with each other and will be entirely irreconcilable. This makes development hard, as decisions may often be met with op-

---

[5]In Adam Davidson's article *Getting Around with Maps and Apps: How ICT Sways Mode Choice*, he notes how a young passenger was very happy that arrival times were displayed at a train station and that he could change his route depending on the arrival time of the next train, while an older passenger thought it was pointless, since he and other passengers will wait for a train on that platform regardless of how long they will have to wait. Meyer, Shaheen 2017 *Disrupting Mobility – Impacts of Sharing Economy and Innovative Transportation on Cities* p.173

position and may be reversed as changes within politics occur, meaning that work may be wasted unnecessarily.

5.2.2 Imperfect Information

In game theory, there is a concept of *perfect information* – this is a situation where all players of a game have instantaneous knowledge of all the market prices in the game, as well as their own utility scores and other measures that can be used to evaluate the scenario. An example of a game with perfect information is Chess, where both players see the positions of all the pieces and what effects they have on other pieces. Transport is certainly not a game with *perfect information* – even with current mapping and routeing technologies that use crowd and delay data, no one knows how the entire spectrum of transport options are affected by the current users and what it will mean for their own journey. The situation for commuters is usually even poorer than that – they will most likely not even know all of the options available to them at all. Any user of mapping and routeing technologies will have probably noticed that occasionally they know a quicker or better route than what is suggested to them. Sometimes new transport services are introduced to areas without many people noticing. New services will often not be providing data to companies that provide maps and routes, meaning that anyone using those technologies will not be aware of these options. When introducing a transport service (or running an existing one), it is often necessary to advertise the existence and benefits of that form of transport to inform any interested people. Any advertising campaign is never going to reach all the relevant people.

The fact that people have a lack of information on their current transport scenario means that people cannot be expected to always use transport options that will actually score highest according to a particular person's values, since they may think the route they are taking is scoring higher due to the lack of real information. This is a nightmare for transport authorities, who cannot know exactly what information is available to which set of people. When authorities do not know what knowledge is available to commuters, they are unable to accurately plan or predict their movement, as applying a change that should change their behaviour may result in no change due to the lack of information.

5.2.3 Irrational Behaviour

A recent realisation in the world has come from economics and behavioural psychology. It turns out that a significant part of the population behaves irrationally[6]. This means, that even if they DID have perfect information on all the transport means available for them, they may still not behave in a manner that would be the best option by their own criteria. This causes a great headache for transport authorities, as they cannot possibly predict what some people will do. A subgroup of transport users can be modelled as "irrational", but what can their behaviour be assigned to be? Changes to a network designed to guide behaviour may have little or no effect on people who are behaving irrationally.

5.2.4 Bad Behaviour

Sometimes behaviour is not even irrational – it is just simply bad. Sometimes schemes that try to change people's behaviour are just going to make things worse, especially when it has already always been obvious

---

[6]An excellent read on this topic is Dan Ariely's *Predictably Irrational* (2008).

the behaviour was not ideal[7]. For example, an introduction of a ban of texting-while-driving in the US resulted in an increase in related insurance claims. This phenomenon is explained by what the Canadian police call *crotching* – continuing texting, but doing it in one's lap so as to reduce the chance of being caught[8]. Scenarios like this raise the question – should the authorities at such a point allow texting-while-driving again, in order to reduce *crotching* and thereby decrease accidents, or should they continue to punish an action that is clearly dangerous? Is the problem the fact that behaviour has become worse as a result of the law, or the fact that the law wasn't enforced well enough in order to prevent the accidents? Should authorities be held responsible for the increase in accidents, or is it clear that the drivers should hold full responsibility? What is the way forwards? The next step could be to increase the punishment for cases of *crotching*. Would that stop the behaviour, or would it lead to actions that could exacerbate the problem.

In some cases, undesirable behaviour can be a symptom of poor communication of authorities. For example, legal drink-driving alcohol limits are often interpreted by people as the approved limits under which it is safe to drive. For example, in England the legal limit is a Blood Alcohol Concentration (BAC) of 0.08%. However, it is very clear from studies that even low quantities of alcohol can affect a driver's reaction

---

[7]Is it entirely obvious? Something I found surprising was that the action of talking and listening on a hands-free or even a handheld phone can decrease risk (although probably not if you are aware of this statistic and react to it [please forget this footnote upon reading]). See Richard J Hanowski's *Behavioural Adaptation and Unintended Consequences* from Christina M. Rudin Brown and Samantha L. Jamson's *Behavioural Adaptation and Road Safety* CRC Press, p.328

[8]Christina M. Rudin-Brown, Brian Jonah and Paul Boase, *Behavioural Adaptation to Road Safety Policy* from Christina M. Rudin Brown and Samantha L. Jamson's *Behavioural Adaptation and Road Safety* CRC Press, p.189

time, balance and judgements of speed and distance. Road safety experts would consider only very low levels (¡0.02% BAC) as safe[9]. A lack of understanding the law – primarily the fact that the legal limit has been set based on a consideration of many factors, of which safety is only one – results in many people therefore thinking that the legal limit is the safety limit[10]. Where people are aware they are under the legal limit and consider themselves safe, advertising campaigns against driving under the influence will fall on deaf ears in the case unless authorities start to make the distinction between legal and safe far more clear.

5.2.5 Uncontrollable Factors

Another major problem for transport authorities is that they do not have control over various factors that can change the situation they are trying to manage. When modelling in preparation for a development, variables that are correlated at the time of modelling may no longer be correct at the time a development is delivered. Ortuzár and Willumsen's Modelling Transport makes the point that *a strong correlation between banana production and car ownership in a particular country may disappear once oil is discovered there*. This is a truly radical change that would change the game for transport modellers entirely. In urban settings there are many factors that are out of Transport authorities' control. Factors that change people's behaviour - from political policies at national levels to local employer policies – can change the transport scenario entirely. Systems improvements for a recent scenario can be entirely useless for the

---

[9]Rudin-Brown, Jonah and Boase *Behavioural Adaptation to Road Safety Policy* from Rudin-Brown and Jamson's *Behavioural Adaptation and Road Safety* p.190.

[10]This can then also lead to the drivers driving illegally in areas where legal limits are lower (e.g. Scotland – ¡0.05% BAC), since they think that they are behaving responsibly and safely.

current scenario.

5.2.6 Noise

Increasing traffic flow also increases the noise on networks. This can be undesirable for people who live in the vicinity of the network and they may therefore be unhappy with an increase in traffic flow in their area. This can be a factor that affects roads, rail and airports. The noise factor can also force routes to change - the Concorde was banned from flying over urban areas due to its sonic boom. Not only human occupants can be affected by noise. For example, studies on birds have shown that it is very likely that birds change the way they sing as a response to traffic noise fluctuations[11].

Noise barriers are now regularly deployed around major roads to decrease the amount of noise pollution in living spaces, but can often look unattractive. Acoustic Green Barriers (glorified hedges) are a particularly excellent approach to reducing noise in areas, while having both aesthetic and environmental benefits.

On the other hand are issues of low noise – electric cars are notably quiet, especially when travelling at a fairly slow pace. People who are trying to cross roads often rely on sound, which is not a sense that would save them from a quiet electric car. Electric cars are therefore now producing sounds (that wouldn't be there naturally) in order to improve safety for people on the roads.

So it seems that we have a strange Goldilocks phenomenon – where too much noise is bad and too little noise is also bad. Authorities are

---

[11] *Evidence of suboscine song plasticity in response to traffic noise fluctuations and temporary road closures* Katherine E. Gentry, Megan F. McKenna, David A. Luther Bioacoustics ¿ The International Journal of Animal Sound and its Recording 17 April 2017 p.26

162

charged with the task of ensuring we have just the right amount of noise, which will of course differ with the range of any population's opinions.

5.2.7 Heat

Heating can also be a problem. For some buses and trains, this can be due to the fact that they need to be heated in Winter to stop people freezing aboard. The other side can be more dangerous though. Urban Métro systems are now often facing huge issues with heating. And it's often not just a simple problem that can be solved with the costs of extra coolers. The heat can be difficult to extract. A cooling fan in an Underground system will need planning permission from councils and people living in neighbourhoods for the vents above ground[12]. A lot of engineering goes into solving this kind of problem. London Underground trains are deliberately designed to not be aerodynamic. Their flat fronts are supposed to push air through the tunnels to help with ventilation[13]. Even so, the London Underground still has considerable problems with the heat in the tunnels over the Summer and is constantly trying new methods to deal with it.

5.2.8 Light

This isn't exactly a problem for many people, but speaking from my own heart, the lighting on the streets can be problematic. I am personally interested in backyard astronomy, but the light pollution from street lights make observing exotic celestial objects difficult. I wish there were more amateur astronomers in the country to make this an issue, but at the

[12]https://www.ianvisits.co.uk/blog/2017/06/10/cooling-the-tube-engineering-heat-out-of-the-underground/

[13]Martin, Andrew *Underground, Overground* p.112

moment I guess it is just an example of a niche issue caused by transport infrastructure.

5.3 Marchetti's Constant

A worry for urban planners and politicians has been the concept of Urban Sprawl. This is the concept that if allowed, cities' suburbs will spread more and more over the rural area around the city. The worry is partly driven by an economic concept called Marchetti's Constant. This concept states that the average commuting time will always approximate to an hour. If transport is developed around the edge of the city - speeding up transport to the city – people will be able to live further away from the city while continuing to be able to travel to work in the same amount of time. It will be possible to live further away, while keeping to the approximate hour commute length. Urban Sprawl is particularly worrying, as the change of rural areas into suburbia can mean a loss of wildlife and their ecosystems, a reduction in agricultural land, a loss of the *countryside feeling* that many people in rural areas love; and all the other effects of destroying a large amount of plant life.

I once attended an event about the future of transport at PA Consulting's offices. The panel was at the time discussing Hyperloop and how it could allow travel from London to Scotland in minutes. Upon asking them what they thought such a transport technology would mean in relation to Marchetti's constant (if it succeeded), I was told that they didn't think it would mean people would buy houses far away from London and work from Scotland, but rather that Londoners may consider working in, or moving to Scotland. The latter option seemed certainly plausible, while the former is not. It is certainly possible that it will be cheaper to live and commute from Scotland than from within London while still working in London, while it is unlikely to be the other way round. If people realise this and start moving to Scotland, house prices will increase there. Anyone living in the area near the new station had better hope that their local job salaries will also increase; otherwise they may only be able to afford to continue to live there if they decide to commute to London.

The thoughts of Urban sprawl may not be the only reason, but city expansion has not always been a policy of government, as can be seen in the Treasury's initial opposition to London's Crossrail project[14]. While it can be a worry, it also needs to be weighed up with the economic benefit of connecting cities. If we go as far back as even the Roman Empire, it is pretty clear that the building of roads and connecting of markets has resulted in increased trade and contributed to making economies thrive. The introduction of trains in the 19th century allowed the transport of fresh goods, such as seafood to inland areas. If travel becomes faster, even more economic possibilities could open up. In this case, economic benefits may need to be weighed up against urban transport issues – what is more important, the economic benefits gained for the areas, or the quality of commutes?

5.4 Other Ways We Can Improve the Journey

Ensuring that everyone is near to a transport connexion is a great way to ensure people's transport options are improved. The journey as a con-

---

[14]*It's not government policy that London should grow, there is not such a policy, so forget Cross-rail* From Simone Busetti's *Governing Metropolitan Transport – Institutional Solutions for Policy Problems*, SpringerBriefs in Applied Sciences and Technology (2015) p.76

cept can be broken down into many segments and improvements can be targeted at different parts of the journey. A simple breakdown of using some mode of public transport could be as follows:

1. Walking to connexion

2. Waiting time

3. Boarding time

4. Travel time

5. Alighting time

6. Walking to Destination

Most people when thinking about transport will mostly be thinking about how transport authorities can improve the waiting time (2) and the travel time (4). But the other parts of a journey can also be improved. 1 and 6 would be improved by increasing the amount of connexions in an area. They are also vastly improved in door-to-door services, for example taxis or London's dial-a-ride buses. Boarding (3) and alighting (5) times will be improved mostly by the design of the vehicle itself. London's old routemaster buses had no doors for entry, meaning that passengers could hop on or off without waiting for the bus to stop. A passenger could walk to the exit to be prepared to jump off when they need to and then jump off precisely at the location they want to. This was certainly a way of shortening the alighting times, but at the cost of increased risk of injury to the passengers[15].

---

[15] For a more detailed discussion of boarding and alighting times, look no further than *Models of bus boarding and alighting dynamics* [Lijun Sun, Alejandro Tirachini, Kay W. Axhausen, Alexander Erath, Der-Horng Lee, *Models of bus boarding and alighting dynamics,*

The breakdown becomes more complex if a journey requires multiple stages. For example, passengers taking a bus into a fairly poorly connected area may want to switch to a taxi service upon arrival at their bus stop. In that case we would have the following breakdown:

1. Walking to bus stop

2. Waiting for the bus

3. Boarding the bus

4. Travelling on the bus

5. Alighting the bus

6. Hailing a taxi

7. Boarding the taxi

8. Travelling on the taxi

9. Alighting taxi

10. Walking to the destination

In this case, 10 should be a pretty short part of the journey, as the taxi can take the passengers very close to their destination. What should be noted here is that the waiting time for the taxi could be vastly improved if people were offered the technology to hire a taxi that would arrive at the precise time that the bus arrived at the bus stop[16]. Or an even more

Transportation Research Part A: Policy and Practice, Volume 69, 2014, Pages 447-460, ISSN 0965-8564, https://doi.org/10.1016/j.tra.2014.09.007].

[16]Here I am inspired by Joe Iacobucci, Kirk Hovenkotter and Jacob Anbinder's article *Transit Systems and the Impacts of Shared Mobility* where they suggest an app that will allow ride sharing at bus destinations with the use of UberPOOL interconnected with bus data (see p.75 of Meyer and Shaheen's Disrupting Mobility – Impacts of Sharing Economy and Innovative Transportation on Cities).

futuristic scenario can be imagined where a taxi could temporarily dock with the bus while in transit, allowing sections 5-7 to become one smooth process, cutting out a significant part of the journey. Of course, such a change to the bus system would be dramatic and would come with many risks and technological challenges. But no-one can stop us from having crazy dreams.

5.5 Infinite Expansion Options

As urban areas continue being developed, the buildings are using up space, leaving little room for transport. Roads that are not wide enough to handle the traffic loads can no longer be expanded without demolishing lines of buildings. If we are to continue expanding our metropolitan transport capabilities, where can the infrastructure go?

5.5.1 Durin's Bane

Many cities around the world have already developed a deep underground rail infrastructure. These networks require tunnels that are at various levels, so that they can cross over each other without slowing down trains on the other lines.

Initially the simplest way to build an underground line is to use the cut-and-cover method. In this method a hole is dug in the ground, and then supported by a structure strong enough to hold a surface above it. These structures can be very strong and can have buildings constructed above them. Unfortunately this method is only practical for a few levels of depth. As trains need to travel ever deeper underground, the amount of material that needs to be removed becomes immense and quite a challenge. The ability to use the cut-and-cover method also depends on the ability to purchase all the land above the designed route, and knocking down any structures already present. In cities like London, there is not much room for such further developments. While various authorities have powers that allow the forced purchasing of land[17], many of the buildings are historical buildings on protected lists that cannot be removed. Many existing infrastructure networks already go under various areas – such as electric cables, water pipes and sewers. Many digs are also likely to come across archaeologically important sites. These problems mean that substantial digging straight from the surface can be hard to get permission for and to enact.

Where cut-and-cover methods are not possible, authorities need to buy, build or hire boring machines[18]. These machines are not so called because they are tedious, but rather because they bore through the ground like moles. These machines are pretty huge – they need to be the diameter of the tunnel they are digging. As they dig, processes need to be set up to remove the waste material from the tunnel and to start lining the walls of the newly made tunnel with materials to strengthen it and stop it collapsing. But the wall linings are not the sole factor holding these tunnels together. The fact that the ground around and above the tunnel has been mostly left untouched means that the pressure across the earth can spread onto the sides of the tunnel, keeping them as steady as a hole pushed by a finger into a wet block of floral foam. These tunnels are so

---

[17]Such as the Mayor or the relevant local authorities, via Compulsory Purchase Orders.

[18]And this is truly in order of descending preference. Cut-and-cover structures will cost 3-5X as much as a rail of the same span built at surface. Once tunnelling is involved, the cost of a line of rail will cost 4-10X as much as the same rail built on the surface. These are considerable differences in price, especially since rail projects are usually on the national scale and will cost billions. Price comparison taken from Goel, Singh & Zhao *Underground Infrastructures: Planning, Design, and Construction* (2012) Elsevier p.128.

strong that they can be used as bomb shelters, and were used as such during World War II. While these boring machines can be incredibly expensive, it is also very expensive and tricky to find a way to lift them out of the tunnels they have dug. As a result, some of them are left buried at the end of the tunnels when a project is finished.

But how deep can we go? Well, there is not much reason to doubt that we could not go really deep. Natural caves can be as deep as the Krubera cave, which is over 2km deep. The deepest man-made mine is the Mponeng gold mine, which is over 4km deep. While such depths are feasible, they are likely to not be really necessary.

Even if trains were running on levels vertically separated by about 50m, this would be over 80 levels. It would be possible to build plenty of lines going north-south on one level, east-west on the next, north-east to south-west on another and north-west to south-east on a fourth one and make it pretty easy to travel in any direction fairly optimally in just 4 levels. Not only would 80 levels be entirely overkill, but it would also be very difficult to maintain, pump water out and circulate cool air in. While travelling downwards can be fairly efficient, lifts or escalators going up to 4km up are going to add additional inefficiencies to the solution of a train going along a horizontal line. Digging so deep would likely cause more problems than it would solve[19]. The digging

---

[19]Including psychological problems – research on underground space use has shown that it can decrease productivity (although it is most damaging to those with the least stimulating jobs), it can double the chance of onset of delirium and can cause depression. Effects on physical and mental health in underground spaces can depend on the building function, amount of freedom of movement, amount of social contact, the size of the space, and the quality of its interior furnishings and nature of lighting. Design is hugely important, with a well-designed entrance being a keystone that can lead to a better experience of the underground space as a whole. See Goel, Singh and Zhao *Underground Infrastructures: Planning, Design and Construction (2012)* Elsevier pp.28-33.

itself would be unprofitable[20], unless our city happened to be lying on vast supplies of rare minerals.

One way or the other, digging downwards is certainly an option. As mentioned before, 4 levels could provide a criss-crossing pattern that could serve all locations across a city. The biggest challenge at this point would be to have entry and exit points frequent, so that the network of tunnels could be accessed easily from the surface. This would require a considerable amount of cooperation of building owners on the surface. Maybe once we have such a complex underground transport network, we may no longer need roads on the surface and could replace them with routes into the tunnels at set intervals[21].

5.5.2 Modular Metropolis

As populations are increasing, more and more skyscrapers tower over cities. Will this continue and develop into cities reminiscent of Blade Runner's LA, Judge Dredd's Mega City One or Metropolis' Metropolis? If so, what will happen to transport? One thing to consider would be how to prepare for the transport needs of the future. As tower blocks get taller, we will start to have similar problems with a large amount of vertical travel being needed in addition to the transverse travel that

---

[20]Although some people claim that underground spaces may be cheaper to develop than overground ones as early as 2050! See Goel, Singh and Zhao Underground Infrastructures: Planning, Design and Construction (2012) Elsevier p.8. It is unclear whether this will be a general truth, or just for sections of underground spaces of a certain size, as current research shows that costs of tunnels increase exponentially with length, according to the formula $C = aL^1.36$ (Underground Infrastructures p.145).

[21]This could be particularly important from the safety perspective. Research in Norway shows that the accident frequency of tunnels is lower than on open roads (0.29 vs 0.43). See Goel, Singh and Zhao Underground Infrastructures: Planning, Design and Construction (2012) Elsevier p.141.

will actually move them between locations. Travel at heights will become necessary, but it may be difficult to implement this after the tower blocks are already built. If authorities are to prepare up front, they may need to start ensuring that tower blocks can support transport infrastructure being attached at a later date. Stronger foundations and additional support structures may need to be considered up front to allow suitable change later. Tower block construction techniques have already reached impressive goals. Particularly exciting is the development of modular buildings such as 461 Dean Street in Brooklyn. The future of modular buildings could see the possibility of increasing the height of buildings as demand requires it. If these buildings could incorporate modules that will allow interfacing with transport networks at heights, transport in dense areas will be able to reach new peaks of efficiency at relative ease of construction.

5.5.3 The Sky is Our Limit

We have had aeroplanes now for over a century now. Yet, they have not yet become affordable to the point of being widely owned by populations. Similarly, helicopters are still out of reach for the average citizen. Gyrocopters may currently be the most available option for the average citizen in terms of a purchase that will allow them flight, cheap versions costing only a bit more than a family car. However, these may only be practical in rural neighbourhoods. Cities have few dedicated landing spaces, which means that there aren't many options of journeys that can be taken. This leaves gyrocopter flying to remain as a hobby or tourist attraction rather than a practical form of transport.

Jet packs, rocket belts and quadcopters have recently been making impressive progress both in terms of abilities and cost. Could this be a way forwards towards affordable air travel for everyone? Traffic at height would not be an issue if commuters could use all 3 dimensions freely. The main problem with flight traffic is usually access to landing sites. But jet packs, rocket belts and quadcopters may need less and less space for landing, meaning almost anywhere can become a landing site. However, while authorities insist on restricting flight over cities to particular paths, it will still be impossible to make any form of flight a part of people's daily commute.

The biggest problem with most of the forms of air travel mentioned so far is that they all require substantial energy for their flight. The energy required to keep the vehicles in the air will mean that these forms of transport will always remain less efficient than transport that only requires force for horizontal movement. However, there are forms of transport that do not require much energy to stay aloft.

Glider planes can be kept in the air for a substantial amount of time by choosing soaring flight paths in rising air. Unfortunately gliders are possibly not the best solution for cities, due to the need of some form of initial boost and a decently sized landing strip. Could these problems be solved? Maybe they could be launched out of the sides of buildings and have some form of docking stations that will decelerate them in a short space without hurting the passengers? It is possible such technology could be achieved, especially if gliders can become lighter and more aerodynamic, allowing slower glide speeds.

Hot air balloons and zeppelins are two further options of flight transport that do not have to use much energy to stay aloft. Balloons are given lift by hot air – usually by burning some form of fuel. In urban environments, it may be possible to provide the heat from systems that are losing heat. For example, air vents cooling underground tunnels could load up air balloons with hot air. Zeppelins on the other hand require a lighter-than-air gas. This used to initially be hydrogen, but catastrophes such as the Hindenburg disaster have dissuaded people from this form of transport[22]. Helium gas has been used more recently, but helium prices are continually rising as it slowly seeps out of the atmosphere into space, diminishing the Earth's supply[23]. Balloons have already historically been moored to buildings, so their interaction with cities isn't based on science-fiction. They may not be very safe in high winds[24], but could be deflated or put away for these periods. They could also be powered by hand, if people were to pull on ropes dangling between buildings. But at that point, it might be better to consider cable cars or zip wires[25].

5.5.4 Malthus mortuus est

The threat of such mass urbanisation does not seem to be looming over us as much as we may think. While people seem to indeed be worried by the prospect of unfettered population growth, it does not seem to be a reality we are likely to face. The fact that birth rates decrease as economies boom and education rises, along with the fact that death rates have not yet started catching up to death rates result in a far likelier prediction that the global population growth will eventually stall. UN projections currently suggest that growth could stop or at least considerably slow as early as 2100, possibly peaking as low as at a population of around

---

[22]Zeppelin enthusiasts argue that most other forms of transport also carry flammable and explosive material (I've certainly seen quite a few cars burn, planes can also explode when faced with fire), but are continually used. Why, they ask, are zeppelins treated unfairly then?

[23]If nuclear fusion becomes effective and profitable, will we have a constant supply of helium?

[24]Especially in the drafts formed between buildings.

[25]Yes, I support zip wires all the way. Why don't we have them already?

10 billion. But even if the global population stops growing, this is not the end of the story for cities. Many cities may continue to grow even if population growth stops. This is due to the phenomenon of *urbanisation* – where rural populations gradually move to urban areas[26]. But even this will eventually have to stop – everyone can only move to the cities once. Maybe this will eventually result in cities full of people and agriculture run by robots, or maybe we will have artificial methods of forming food[27] and land outside of cities will be left entirely for wildlife. Either way, urban population growth will eventually stop.

Whether this means development will stop is a different question – there is a possibility that the demand for additional facilities will continue to grow. But it is difficult to see why this should continue indefinitely either – technological advances should continually make it simpler to repurpose buildings at short notice. But our fears of eternal urban growth seem to be unfounded – cities will reach limits. Once these limits are reached, we may be left with the cities we will have from then on indefinitely. Should we be trying to think ahead, predicting and planning for what we expect the cities to end up as, or should we be trying to solve the current problems - as they are - with what tools we have available?

---

[26]As cities have grown, new terms for them have been needed. Cities that have a population of 10 million or over are referred to as *megacities* and when the population reaches 20 million, they become *metacities* [David Banister, David Bonilla, Moshe Givoni and Rubin Hickman *Transport and development – what Next* from their *Handbook on transport and development* p.678]

[27]Not necessarily chemical – I'm just very hopeful about vertical farming.

5.6 Where Should We Be Improving First?

This book has already identified how prioritisation is an important concept in transport management. However, the ability to understand and figure out where transport needs to improve first isn't just a skill that is useful for authorities. Private companies that can develop methods to understand transport demand and how they can help meet it will be able to provide services and profit[28].

How would one go about finding where additional transport modes or infrastructure could be profitably installed? There are in fact many things to consider. To begin with, it is important to understand the general supply and demand in an area. Are buses and trains overflowing? This can be an indicator that there is room for additional transport operators to profit from the area. But it may also not necessarily be so simple. For example, buses may be overflowing during peak time, but buses travelling during off-peak times may be almost empty, for the vast majority of the day. Building up capability to handle peak times can be beneficial, but there are additional costs associated with then running (or not running) those buses for the off-peak times. Peak times are often also directional. Buses and trains travelling towards a city centre can be overcrowded in the morning, but the buses leaving the city centre for the suburbs may be empty. A bus travelling during peak time in these conditions will therefore on average be only half full. In many cases, the small amount of passengers for most of the day and in the opposite direction to

---

[28]CityMapper have written about how they use their analysis tool "Simcity" to identify gaps in cities' transport networks by using the data acquired from their mapping app https://medium.com/citymapper/cm2-night-rider-our-first-commercial-bus-route-d9d7918be899

the main bulk of commuters may bring the cost efficiency of the service down by a considerable amount. Transport operators regularly analyse their service to try and increase profit, so if there was additional profit to be made by adding vehicles to a route, they would certainly do it, unless their analysis was incorrect. Starting a transport business based on simple supply and demand models therefore requires some sort of evidence that the existing services are running sub optimally. There is no reason to not think that this is the case in many scenarios, but careful analysis needs to be made to ensure that the introduction of a new service doesn't just result in failure.

When attempting to introduce a new transport service, one must first identify what service is actually needed by the customers. Why would customers switch to this new service, rather than use the current one? If one were to offer a new bus service on an already existing route with fares that are not too steep, it is very likely that passengers could be acquired, simply due to the fact that they are taking the route anyway and that there are buses that may currently be more spacious than on the existing service. However, depending on the local authority, it may not be allowed for an operator to operate the exact same route as another operator. This can be understandable. When I was studying in Sheffield, I would frequently take a bus service that was served by two bus operators (First and StageCoach). The prices on the two services could differ and a return ticket would only be accepted on the service it was bought on. For many people, this was beneficial - bus wars between operators meant that prices could remain low. If the bus operators ran a joint return ticket, it would be likely to be more expensive than the specific return ticket. The return ticket for a specific operator can remain at a low cost, because the operator has in that case ensured that the customer will return to their service, or pay without using it, meaning that they have gained a future security for their sole benefit. A return ticket joint over multiple operators would mean that no benefit over their competition would be secured. However, a joint ticket could also be beneficial for the operators. If the fares of the ticket were shared, it is possible for an operator that someone buying a return ticket may take the other operator's service on the way back, leaving room for an additional paying customer on that service. For many people, the lack of standardisation of the ticketing was annoying - some would avoid taking the bus altogether due to this reason. Simplicity makes ticketing easier and more understandable for customers, which can encourage customers to use a service. This realisation has meant that some cities are opting for one fare for all buses in an attempt to increase bus usage and make travel easier for customers.

Market analysis is very important in transport. Understanding where people are travelling to and why is essential to figuring out where a service may be successful. For example, many people may be taking a bus A, followed by a bus B due to the fact that there are no alternative means of easily reaching their destination. These buses may travel in a zigzag and actually reach their destination in quite a sizeable amount of time. In my youth, I was able to jog across West London from Northolt to Hampton Hill (about 10 miles) in less time than I could reach it via public transport. This was simply because there was no direct route and public transport had to be taken by an assortment of zigzags. But that doesn't necessarily mean that creating such a direct route would be successful. There has to be enough market interest in order to make the service profitable. It should be kept in mind that the market interest for a route will not be just for a journey between two particular points - the market interest could be for any point along that route. It could also be an interest in arriving at a variety of points that may suddenly be better reached by the new route.

A new service that may go along some new potential route will then have to be analysed to see how well it is likely to capture the market that it is targeting. A good way to do this would be to figure out a competitiveness index[29] for various points on and around the route of the new service. A competitiveness index can be acquired by running a survey on and around your planned route. The people taking part in the survey should be asked to give scores as to how much they value different factors of their transport options (e.g. cost, journey time, space). These scores can then be used to figure out an average weighting as to how much each of the factors matter to the potential customers. Once these weighting are acquired, one can now empirically compare how likely people are to favour the new service over existing services by comparing how the factors differ amongst services, adjusted by the weightings.

To gain an even better estimate of what may happen if the new service is introduced, it might be better to refine this analysis further. Results from the survey could be sorted into groups and analysed separately. They could be separated by area, by preferences or by other data. When these smaller groups are then analysed, it is likely that more accurate predictions can be reached. This is a result of the fact that a general average may not in fact be that useful. For example, there may be two groups of people, one set of which care the most about costs of journeys and will always prefer to walk rather than take other forms of transport, while the other does not care about the cost of journey, but wants the quickest pos-

---

[29]Jurewicz, Piotr (et al.) *Method for Assessing Rail Transport Competitiveness in Poland and the United Kingdom, Transport Development Challenges in the Twenty-First Century.*

sible journey, which they feel they can only achieve by driving their own cars. An average of these groups may result in a competitiveness index that suggests a bus route along their route will be successful, as the cost factor will be averaged out between them. In the meantime, the reality will remain that these are two radically different groups who would both avoid the new bus service. In this case, this information is not particularly useful for the analysis and these groups could be discarded while trying to figure out what market could gain from a new service.

Similarly, it may be the case that a particular type of bus cannot really accommodate a substantial amount of people in the area who may have disabilities. Here is an untapped market group that may require a service that fits their specific situations.

As groups are broken down further, the distinctions can be used to better analyse the market and improve on a transport service.

In transport modelling it is common to try to break down groups as much as possible when modelling transport networks. Ultimately it would be best if every single person's journey could be understood and analysed - that would give the best information for planning a new transport service. Models that break down groups substantially are called *disaggregate* models and are now used widely instead of the simple *aggregate* models that would have been used in the past.

5.6.1 Monopolies and Market Shares

Transport authorities may also be interested in bringing in new transport services for other reasons, than just the fact of simple profit. One of the reasons may be to break up monopolies. Breaking up monopolies can be useful to ensure transport can thrive through healthy competition between transport providers. In areas served by competing providers, costs are likely to decrease and productivity is likely to increase. Operators are also likely to start considering providing options for people who may not be served particularly well in order to increase their market size. At worst, commuters will at least be able to have an option between types of services. These points may seem obvious, but what is less obvious is what a transport monopoly consists of and how it can be found.

Typically a monopoly is when there is some exclusive control of a supply in a market. In the case of transport, this isn't necessarily just about whether the entire rail network is owned by one company (or nationalised). Monopolies in transport can exist at the local level, and even in sub-divisions at that level. We can talk about transport monopolies over particular routes in fact. If a person is travelling between point A and B and they only have one significant option (i.e. out of their desired walking distance), there is a monopoly on their journey.

How would you go about figuring out where transport monopolies are occurring? One way would be to take a map of an area and to draw dots equally spaced across it. For any selection of two points, an analysis can be run of how many options there are to travel between them, and what share of commuters on this route each option is likely to hold. Indices such as the Herfindahl-Hirschman Index can then be used on this information to measure the amount of competition on each point-to-point journey. Areas (points where most routes leading away from them have little competition) or routes with low competition can then be targeted for new services.

5.6.2   Economies of Scale

While scale is often advantageous and may seem limitlessly so in many modern companies (especially technological companies), economies of scale are not so simple in transport operations. As the size of a transport operation grows, maintenance, communications and organisation can become very complex and expensive. Transport companies will generally benefit a lot from initial growth in scale of operations, but will reach an optimal size after which additional growth may not be worth the additional investment or they may not even be profitable.

5.6.3   Public or Private

Should transport be operated privately or fully publicly? Is there a sweet spot in between? This is a topic that has got more complexities than I can account for in such a short book. However, I think it is worth considering whether those calling for one or the other are just assuming the grass is green on the other side. From what I have seen, success and costs of journeys don't seem entirely related to whether operators are private or public. For example, Sweden and Germany saw reduced costs after introducing competitive tendering. Meanwhile, Britain has seen rising costs with competitive tendering (where frequently renegotiated contracts lead to fairly stable costs, while rarely negotiated contracts rise in cost over time)[30]. If the same strategy has seen different results in different countries, one should surely look to different factors as to why the results differ.

---

[30] Andrew Smith, Phill Wheat and Michal Wolanski *Public transport operations costs* from Chris Nash' *Handbook of Research Methods and Applications in Transport Economics and Policy (2017)* p.60.

Construction works on fixed links have been shown to have overrun costs on state-owned projects by 3 times as much as on private projects[31]. However, overrun costs were also twice as large on high-speed rail as they were on urban rail for state owned rail constructions. Such comparisons of costs seem to me personally rather facile and I'm not personally convinced they hold much weight. Almost every rail construction, project and operation is unique and difficult to compare to others. Public and private projects can also both differ vastly in their business models. Statistical errors can occur for vast amounts of reasons – such as missing the fact that private companies only need to pick up work they consider profitable, while public sector transport organisations may have to consider work that is not.

Countries that have a mixture of privately and publicly owned rail have the advantage that organisational actions can happen on a case by case basis. It is possible to switch ownership on particular underperforming instances. It can also be possible for the state to compete against private companies for projects, meaning that if a nationalised operation is cheaper or more efficient, it will be naturally picked through the procurement process. In principal, the state should also have a stronger hand for negotiations if it does not have to rely on the private sector to pick up projects and operations.

A common misconception (one I saw stated and shared rather frequently during the UK 2019 general election campaign) is that nationalisation naturally means cheaper fares for passengers. This is incorrect

---

[31]Chantal C. Cantarelli and Bent Flyvbjerg *Decision-making and major transport infrastructure projects: the role of project ownership* from Robin Hickman, Moshe Givoni, David Bonilla and David Banister's *Handbook on Transport and Development (2017)* Elgar Online, p.385.

– the main factor that changes the price of fares is not the ownership of operations or assets, but the amount of subsidisation the rail network receives[32]. Rail networks do not require national ownership to be subsidised, so if the population decides they prefer their rail fares to be paid through taxation of the whole population, their government can do this without changing the ownership of assets and operations at all. The rail industry can (and often is) subjected to a large amount of scrutiny and regulations, ensuring that whoever is responsible for work on it will charge fairly and will be accountable for any failures.

5.7 Urban Design

A recent approach to transport has been the thought that the design of neighbourhoods, towns and cities are what drive how people will behave and what forms of transport they will use. Analysts speak of the 5 Ds when investigating the effects of urban design – Density, Diversity, Design, Destination accessibility and Distance to transit[33]. Areas that are Denser can mean that people are more likely to get to a destination in a short amount of time, and may be able to walk or to cycle there. This is not the case however, if there is little land use Diversity – if there are no jobs, shops or other features and resources in the area that the population is interested in (i.e. little Destination Accessibility), they may need to take other means of transport to reach an area that does have

---

[32]It is also worth noting that rail subsidisation does not all go into subsidising fares. Subsidisation of the rail industry will be split between some subsidisation of fares and subsidisation of development and improvement of the infrastructure.

[33]Philip Stoker, Susan Petheram and Reid Ewing *Urban structure and travel*, from Robin Hickman, Moshe Givoni, David Bonilla and David Banister's *Handbook on Transport and Development (2017)* Elgar Online, p.27.

them. The Design of the area (the block size, number of intersections etc.), along with the local Distance to transit (i.e. how nearby are the bus stops and train stations?) can similarly affect commuter behaviour.

As authorities have learnt that there are such relations to transport behaviour, they have started considering how they can apply this knowledge to improve transport services. A key movement has been *New Urbanism*, which is an urban design movement that seeks to encourage walking and cycling by creating neighbourhoods with a wide range of housing and job types. The success of this movement is still debated amongst urban planners, with both advocates and critics on all sides of the political spectrum. For example, the concepts are criticised both for restricting private enterprise and for being a deregulatory force in support of private sector developers.

While New Urbanism may seem to make logical sense, it is not clear whether there is evidence that changing urban design actually changes the behaviour of citizens. For example, the case might be that people are not changing behaviour, but rather that people who already live in a particular lifestyle are moving to areas that permits that lifestyle[34]. While increased density does seem to lead to a reduction of car use, increased residential density does not change average trip distances and increased employment density has shown to actually increase trip distances[35]. While built environment characteristics of the residential lo-

---

[34]Evidence was shown that particularly people who choose their home location for a shorter commute, cyclists and whites (it was a US study) are the most likely to move to the same neighbourhood type. Kevin J. Krizek, Ahmed El-Geneidy and Ryan Wilson *How stable are preferences for neighbourhood type and design in residential moves* from Robin Hickman, Moshe Givoni, David Bonilla and David Banister's *Handbook on Transport and Development (2017)* Elgar Online, p.27.

[35]Marcial Echenique and Alastair Donald *New urbanism and travel* from Robin Hickman, Moshe Givoni, David Bonilla and David Banister's *Handbook on Transport and Development*

cation may affect travel behaviour to some extent, a large part of the behaviour will still be driven by individual and household characteristics
and the resultant attitudes towards housing and neighbourhoods and
travel preferences[36].

To encourage people to walk and cycle[37], authorities need to not just
implement town planning policies that allow it and make it desirable.
They also need to encourage it by other means. Emotional and commu-
nal motivation stemming from personal characteristics and the community's social norms are just as likely to be instrumental to this change
of behaviour[38]. Whether it could work or not, many people oppose any
such schemes aimed at changing the populace's behaviour. In a democ-
racy, is it the government's job to change the behaviour of the people, or
vice versa?

Urban design can have an effect on transport behaviour, but transport options can also drive design and development. In London we have
the example of how the Thatcher government prioritised the Jubilee Line
Extension through North Greenwich to Stratford in the hope of developing the derelict Docklands area[39]. While development there seemed to
stall for years[40], 30 years later the area is now flourishing, with tower

---

(2017) Elgar Online, p.116.

[36] Bert van Wee and Patricia Mokhtarian *The role of attitudes in accounting for self-selection effects* from Robin Hickman, Moshe Givoni, David Bonilla and David Banister's *Handbook on Transport and Development (2017)* Elgar Online, p.169.

[37] Called *Active Travel* in the industry

[38] Susan Handy *Community Design and Active Travel* from Robin Hickman, Moshe Givoni, David Bonilla and David Banister's *Handbook on Transport and Development (2017)* Elgar Online p.199

[39] Peter Jones *Assessing the wider impacts of the Jubilee Line Extension in East London* from Robin Hickman, Moshe Givoni, David Bonilla and David Banister's *Handbook on Transport and Development p.318*

[40] At least partly due to the Millenium Dome (now the O2 Arena) failing to attract the

blocks being built in North Greenwich and Stratford being used as the Olympic park in the 2012 Summer Olympics, followed by a redevelopment into housing. These areas may not be considered as such excellent development areas if they had not been connected to the rest of London so well – particularly by the Jubilee Line.

5.8   Sustainability

A lot could be written about sustainability, and I will be unusual in only writing on it shortly. Awareness of sustainability is pretty good right now and I'd probably have to write a whole book to add any contributions to this area.

It is obvious now that it is very important to switch to sustainable energy sources. What is less mentioned is the wider perspective on sustainability. Not only energy, but materials in general should be sourced sustainably. Reuse of machinery and structures should be paramount. Where this is not possible, materials should be recycled.

Materials that cannot be sourced sustainably should be dropped. And this is going to be a factor that grows more and more as the demand for various rare elements are needed for all sorts of items.

People and their labour should also have a sustainable approach taken to them. People should never be treated as waste, and neither should their work. Care should be taken to upskill people, to make sure they are paid fairly for their work, and kept healthy and happy. Companies may see this outlook as expensive, but they are most likely not calculating the costs of the loss of expertise as they cycle through employees and providers.

---

expected amount of visitors.

5.9 Independence

The years 2021-2023 saw a huge global supply chain crisis. The crisis was caused by first the changes in labour due to the COVID-19 pandemic, and then by the 2022 Russian Invasion of Ukraine. The crisis was hardest felt in the electronics sector, where it became difficult to buy many items that used to be in abundance in shops across the globe.

Transport systems require a huge amount of resources and therefore thought needs to be put into how to ensure the supply chain of materials is safe from risk. The belief in globalism has for many years meant that supply chains rely entirely on foreign nations. Risk was only considered in diversifying providers. But it is clear that if sourcing was available more locally, countries could have come out of the global supply chain crisis as clear market winners. We can only wait and see whether local sourcing becomes more common as a result or whether nations have not learned their lessons.

5.10 Resilience

The Russian invasion of Ukraine in 2022 has been absolutely disastrous. At the time of writing it is still not over and we all live in hope that peace can be restored to the region.

What is interesting about the effects on Ukrainian citizens is that they are becoming incredibly self sufficient. Many people now have generators and backup internet providers in their homes. The infrastructure systems have out of necessity become incredibly efficient and can fix energy issues or transport network damages due to missiles in a matter of days, and often even in just a few hours.

It is difficult to imagine this level of resilience being common in countries that don't need it at the time. A road can be fixed in Ukraine from an entirely unusable state to a working road in almost no time at all, while many areas of London continue being riddled by potholes half a decade after they first became a nuisance. However, if a country like Ukraine could reach this level of resilience in times of peace, their response to an actual war could be quicker. It isn't something people want to worry about, but Vegetius' adage of *therefore let him who desires peace prepare for war* still stands. Resilience in a nation's transport system is a vital part of a defence strategy, since warfare is highly dependant on logistics, and we must not forget this.

5.11   Reliability

Too many additional developments can result in an unreliable system. Infrastructure has to be expanded slowly. The need for reliability also means that there are always additional costs needed to be covered to ensure that everything runs smoothly. It's no use having a huge and complex metropolitan transport network if it is entirely unreliable.

Perhaps some people may wonder why this is mentioned separately to efficiency. They are not the same. A transport network can be very efficient in terms of how many people it can get across it, but be very unreliable, by only meeting peak efficiency a small amount of the time. Very efficient systems can sometimes involve more complexity and therefore cause more issues when something goes wrong and be harder to fix and put back into the peak state.

Many people would perhaps prefer reliability than efficiency. A lower efficiency of a transport network can potentially result in fewer people using it. They will make different plans, and their plans will not be ruined. An unreliable transport network can ruin the plans of all the people on it and cause turmoil.

5.12 Pollution

Pollution is getting worse throughout the world, and transport authorities are some of the individuals that can reduce pollution the most. Increasing infrastructure in a city can increase pollution, either by promoting driving for road users, or by increasing particulate matter due to the engineering works, the wheels and general commotion.

Solutions for pollution are also not entirely simple. For example, it is a common misconception to assume that with the improvement of technology, fuel efficiency of cars could increase by a significant amount and therefore reduce emissions by a large amount. The reason that this is a misconception is that any change in a market has side effects that will change the market in the future. In this case, an increase in the fuel efficiency of cars would be very likely to increase the amount of cars in the market and the amount they are used, thereby negating the positive effect of the improvement of fuel efficiency. This is called the Jevons Effect – it is named after a nineteenth-century economist who predicted that more efficient coal-fired electricity would mean more coal was needed, rather than less[41]. Will the Jevons effect on transport ever end? Surely eventually energy efficiency will reach a point where everyone can have

---

[41] Peter Newman and Jeff Kenworthy *Urban passenger transport energy consumption and carbon dioxide emissions* from Robin Hickman, Moshe Givoni, David Bonilla and David Banister's *Handbook on Transport and Development (2017)* p.52. This article also presents clear evidence that improving traffic flow doesn't save time for the average driver, meaning that energy consumption won't decrease either.

their own vehicle and take it everywhere where they would like to go, meaning no additional transport could be needed. This would mean that there would be little reason to increase trip lengths or journey amounts with additional efficiency improvements. This certainly may well be the case one day, but at that point it is also possible that space travel may have become efficient enough to be accessible to many people. Then the effect will be seen once more.

Studies that show clear improvements available with changes of regulations also occasionally fail due to behavioural or environmental change. As a result of a study on the A13 motorway that showed an improvement in air quality with an enforced speed limit of 80km/h, the Dutch government installed four sections of motorway with strongly enforced variable message signs. Drivers changed their behaviour drastically, reducing use of the outer lane, increasing traffic jams and driving in 4th gear, ultimately increasing emissions till the authorities increased the speed limit to 100km/h in peak hours[42].

5.13   Conclusion

In this book we have explored a variety of problems, branches of science, and models within those branches. But we have only touched the surface of a selection of problems in transport.

I am hoping that this book has taught you something new. Ideally this will not just be a selection of facts and theories, but also a more careful approach to problems; an understanding that solutions may only

---

[42]Willmink, I., van Arem, B., de Jong, R., Martens, M., van der Horst, R. and Gense, R. 2006.   *Evaluatie en advise filevorming 80km zones.*   TNO-Notitie 06.34.15/NO53/034.65112/IW/YR. TNO, Delfth, The Netherlands

work in the short term, or that they may have side-effects that can make a situation worse; and a new interest in the details of the decisions that authorities have to make. If we want to improve our society and transport, we must first develop our humility by understanding where we currently are and the vast amount of work that was necessary to get us there.

It is by understanding the past that we can make improvements for the future – by studying past decisions and their effects, then applying new thought and data that was not available to us before. George Santayana said that *those who do not learn history are doomed to repeat it,* but he didn't cover the full picture. Studying all of history won't save you from making brand new and shiny mistakes. Studying history may also confuse you as to which historical case is similar to yours, leading you to repeat a mistake anyway. There are many problems in the world of transport and they certainly need to be solved. However, absolute care needs to be taken and we should try not to make rash decisions – we don't want our solutions to cause far worse problems down the line. I couldn't agree more with G.K. Chesterton's statement when he writes that *the business of Progressives is to go on making mistakes. The business of Conservatives is to prevent mistakes from being corrected.* Changes ought to be made, but with a sufficient amount of care.

If you - the reader - like difficult problems and want to have a high impact on the world, please consider the transport sector. Whether you do or don't, I hope what you have read here may inspire you and guide you to work conscientiously towards a better future.